MOLECULAR GASTRONOMY BY MOLECULE-R

AN INTRODUCTION TO THE SCIENCE BEHIND 40 SPECTACULAR RECIPES

Copyright © 2014, 2013 by MOLECULE-R Flavors Inc.
ISBN : 978-0-9921110-1-4

SECOND EDITION - 2014

MOLECULE-R Flavors Inc.
2255A, Dandurand St.
Montreal (Qc) Canada
H2G 1Z3

MOLE
CULE
R

MOJITO
R-EVOLUTION

MOLECULAR
MIXOLOGY KIT

ENSEMBLE DE MIXOLOGIE
MOLÉCULAIRE

Net Wt 0.07 lb (32 g)

MOLE
CULE
R

COSMOPOLITAN
R-EVOLUTION

MOLECULAR
MIXOLOGY KIT

ENSEMBLE DE MIXOLOGIE
MOLÉCULAIRE

Net Wt 0.07 lb (32 g)

MOLE
CULE
R

MOLE
CULE
R

CUISINE
R-EVOLUTION

MOLECULAR
GASTRONOMY KIT

ENSEMBLE DE CUISINE
MOLÉCULAIRE

INCLUDES
20 ADDITIVES SACHETS

6 ESSENTIAL TOOLS

INCLUT
20 SACHETS D'ADDITIFS

6 OUTILS INDISPENSABLES

DVD OF 50 VIDEO RECIPES   DVD DE 50 RECETTES VIDÉO

Net Wt 0.12 lb (55 g)

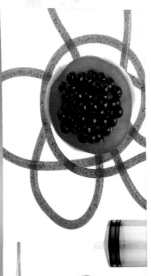

ARO
R-EV

MARGARITA R-EVOLUTION

MOLECULAR
MIXOLOGY KIT

ENSEMBLE DE MIXOLOGIE
MOLÉCULAIRE

Net Wt 0.07 lb (32 g)

SIPHON R-EVOLUTION

CULINARY WHIPPER
WARM AND COLD

SIPHON ALIMENTAIRE
CHAUD ET FROID

Net Wt 1.23 oz (35 g)

VOLATILE FLAVORING & PAIRING KIT

ENSEMBLE D'AROMATISATION VOLATILE

NEW

MOLECULE-R.COM

AROMA R-EVOLUTION

THE AROMAFORK™ AND ITS SET OF 21 AROMAS OFFER A FASCINATING OLFACTIVE EXPERIENCE THAT WILL TRICK YOUR MIND AND MIGHT EVEN CHANGE FOREVER THE WAY YOU PERCEIVE FLAVORS !

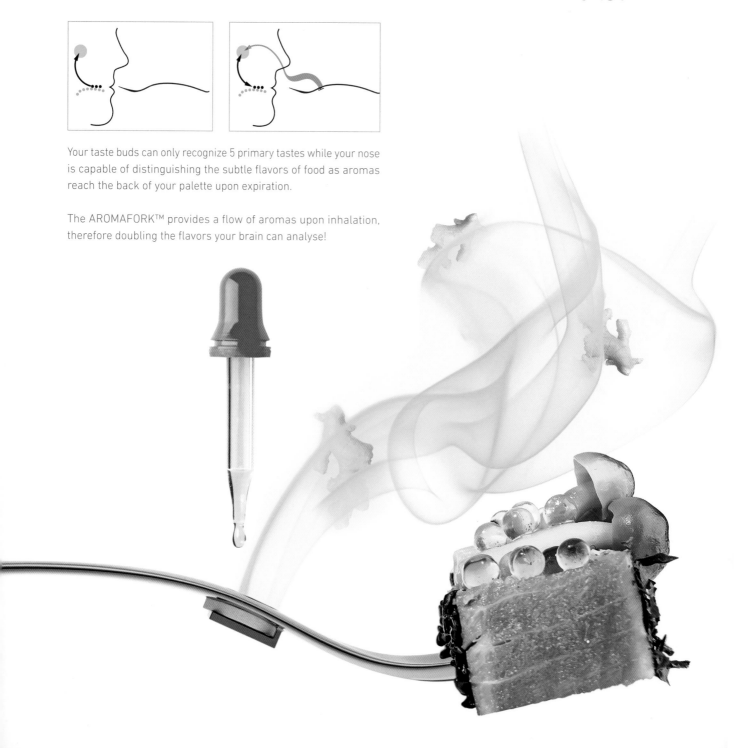

Your taste buds can only recognize 5 primary tastes while your nose is capable of distinguishing the subtle flavors of food as aromas reach the back of your palette upon expiration.

The AROMAFORK™ provides a flow of aromas upon inhalation, therefore doubling the flavors your brain can analyse!

EACH KIT CONTAINS EVERYTHING YOU NEED TO EXPERIMENT WITH VOLATILE FLAVORING.

4 AROMAFORKS™, 21 AROMAS, 4 PIPETTES AND 50 DIFFUSING PAPERS.

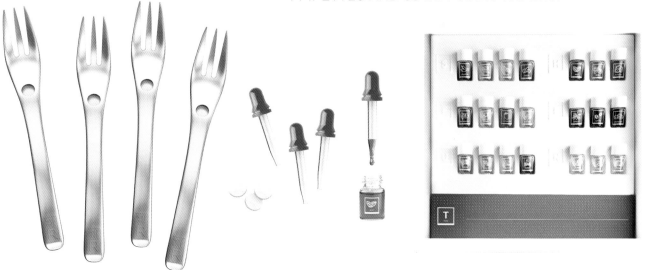

CUISINE R-EVOLUTION

EVERYTHING YOU NEED TO EXPERIMENT
WITH MOLECULAR GASTRONOMY AT HOME.

4 NATURAL FOOD ADDITIVES IN PRE-MEASURED SACHETS
AGAR-AGAR, CALCIUM LACTATE, SODIUM ALGINATE AND SOY LECITHIN.

A 50-RECIPE DVD AND 6 SPECIALIZED TOOLS.

TABLE OF CONTENTS

GELIFICATION RECIPES

SPHERIFICATION RECIPES

EMULSIFICATION RECIPES

OTHER TRANSFORMATIONS RECIPES

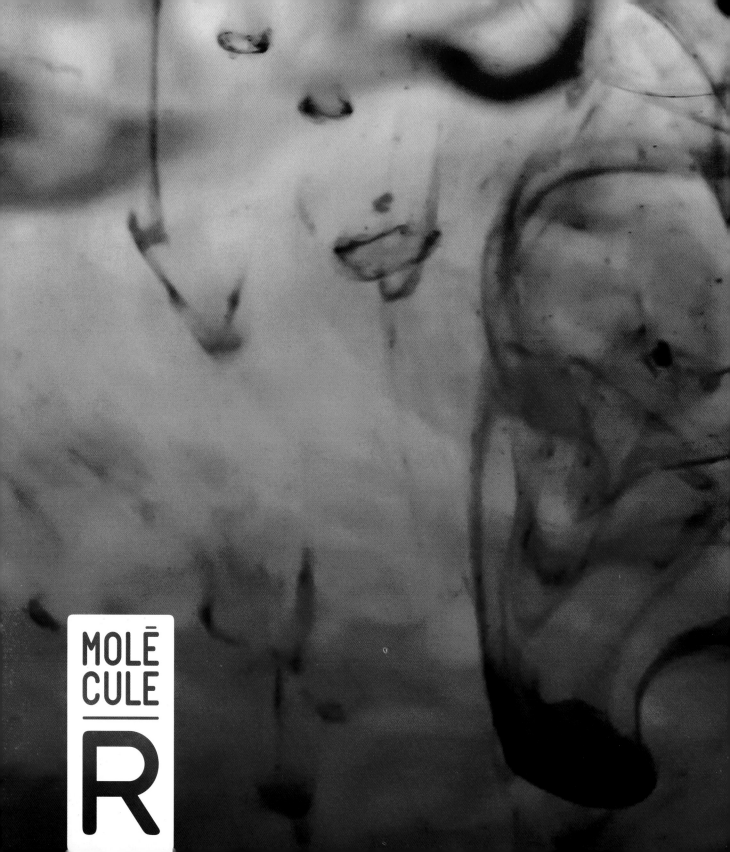

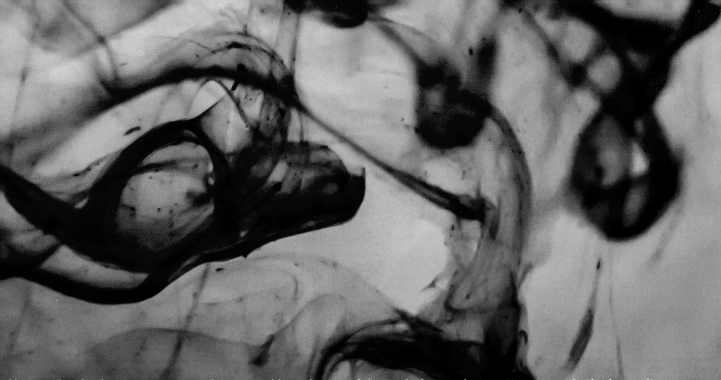

New technologies are now more integrated into the world of arts than ever before. Multimedia displays are set up in sculptures and exhibited in museums; the unexpected strength of new materials makes it possible to push the boundaries of architecture; and the public can now decide the ending of certain theatre plays using their smartphones.

The culinary arts are no exception to this trend and creative chefs are now inspired to incorporate cooking techniques and ingredients borrowed from the world of food science. For more than a decade, renowned, award-winning restaurants have been serving exotically flavored caviar, colorful, gravity-defying foams, bubbles that explode with flavors or even recreations of complex dishes in the form of simple spaghetti.

Obviously, the application of modern cooking techniques does not ensure a successful dish, but, as in all art forms, new technologies support the artistic process by allowing the artist to push creative boundaries. Like any artist, creative chefs provide their audience with an experience, and regardless of the technique, what matters most is the intensity of this experience.

Arising from the fusion of food science with culinary arts, molecular gastronomy is a gourmet trend whose artisans embrace innovation in order to create dishes that are truly multi-sensorial experiences. This cuisine is not at all opposed to the great culinary traditions; instead, it builds on past achievements and broadens the horizons by using resolutely modern techniques and ingredients. A new culinary era has arrived and is now accessible to amateur chefs!

MOLECULE-R PAVES THE WAY FOR A DEMOCRATIZATION OF MOLECULAR GASTRONOMY.

MOLECULAR TECHNIQUES

Molecular gastronomy by MOLECULE-R provides accessibility to spectacular transformation techniques at home.

GELIFICATION

SCULPT FLAVORS INTO TASTY PEARLS, RAVIOLI OR SPAGHETTIS.

SPHERIFICATION

ENCAPSULATE FLAVORS INTO BUBBLES THAT BURST IN YOUR MOUTH.

EMULSIFICATION

CREATE COLORFUL FOAMS THAT INTENSIFY AROMAS.

SIPHON WHIPPING

ADD A CREAMY TOUCH TO YOUR DESSERTS, APPETIZERS AND SIDE DISHES.

SUSPENSION

DEFY GRAVITY BY GIVING FLAVORS A SUSPENDED TWIST.

POWDERIZING

TRANSFORM ANY FATTY INGREDIENT INTO A LIGHT FLAVORED POWDER.

DEEP FREEZING

COOK WITH THE COLD OR CREATE INCOMPARABLY SMOOTH ICE CREAM.

FOOD
ADDITIVES

Research in food preservation is not a new development. Human beings have always sought to preserve foodstuffs first by chilling, drying or smoking meat, then by adding salt, vinegar and sugar. However, industrialization and the movement of populations to cities led to a completely different need: feeding thousands of people with fresh, processed, practical products that are stable during transportation and storage while retaining their organoleptic qualities. So-called "food additives" were gradually introduced to accommodate manufacturers throughout the food chain, but also to meet consumer demands for high-quality products.

Today, the term "food additive" covers nearly 2,500 chemicals that are added to foods for specific purposes such as preserving or processing and enhancing flavor or color. The use of additives in the food processing industry has become so widespread that they are now consumed on a daily basis by the general population.

This list includes coloring, stabilizers, acidifiers, preservatives, enzymes and texturing agents, but it is this last class of food additives that brings great pleasure to molecular gastronomy enthusiasts by creating culinary extravaganzas with unexpected surprises every time!

To share their passion for culinary creativity and experimentation, the young, dynamic team at MOLECULE-R Flavors has developed a complete line of texturing agents for amateur cooks to recreate some of the most spectacular techniques derived from molecular gastronomy. The cuisine of highly creative chefs is now accessible to everyone!

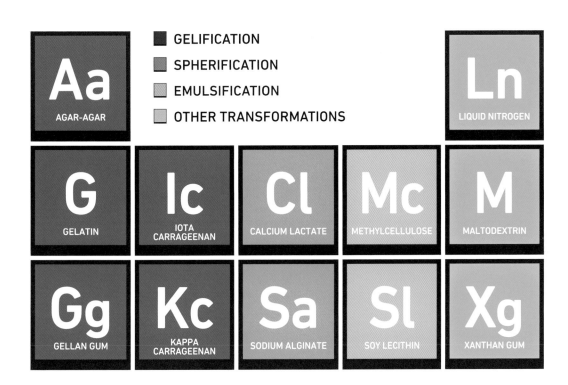

GELIFICATION

SPHERIFICATION

EMULSIFICATION

OTHER TRANSFORMATIONS

Aa AGAR-AGAR

Natural gelling agent extracted from red algae often used to create solid pearls, gel spaghettis and jellies.

Ic IOTA CARRAGEENAN

Natural gelling agent extracted from red algae and used to produce gels with a soft and elastic texture.

Cl CALCIUM LACTATE

Calcium salt used with sodium alginate in the process of spherification.

Mc METHYLCELLULOSE

Natural emulsifier derived from cellulose, used to create denser foams and, when exposed to heat, to create gels that will melt as they cool down.

Ln LIQUID NITROGEN

A major component of air used in its liquid form to create the smoothest ice cream and cook with the cold.

G GELATIN

Cold soluble gelatin that has the same textural properties and melt-in-the mouth effect as traditional gelatin.

Kc KAPPA CARRAGEENAN

Natural gelling agent extracted from red algae and used to produce gels with a firm and brittle texture.

Sa SODIUM ALGINATE

Natural gelling agent extracted from brown algae often combined with a calcium salt in the process of spherification.

Sl SOY LECITHIN

Natural emulsifier extracted from soybeans, often used to shape watery solution into airs.

M MALTODEXTRIN

Unsweet sugar mostly used in creative cooking as an aroma carrier, in the form of tasty powder that can be sprinkled over food preparations and dishes.

Gg GELLAN GUM

Gelling agent obtained via fermentation and used to produce firm gels that slice cleanly & withstand high temperatures.

Xg XANTHAN GUM

Natural thickener derived from glucose via fermentation often used to stabilize emulsions and thicken sauces and drinks.

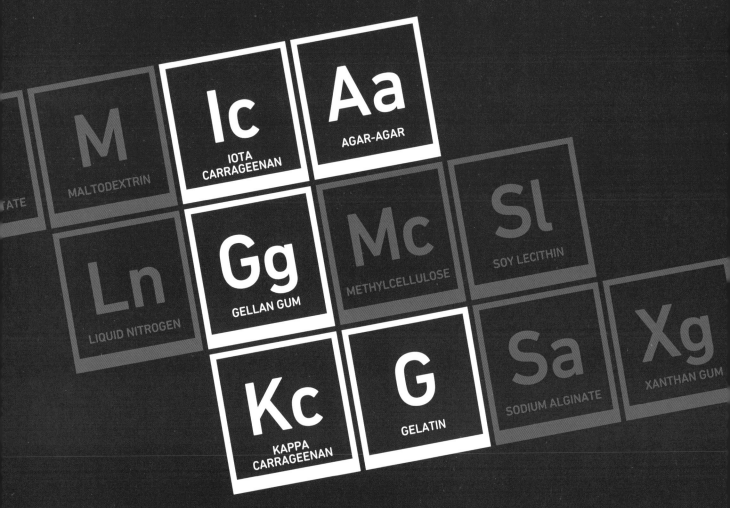

GELIFICATION

Definition and technique

GELIFICATION

The formation of a gel is one of the most common techniques in the industry. However, there is a tendency to disregard the great diversity of gels that can be made in cooking. Depending on the nature and concentrations of the gelling agent being used, the gel texture can range from supple and elastic to firm and brittle. This enables inventive cooks to experiment and attain the exact desired texture!

Despite the wide range of possible textures, the formation of a gel can simply be defined as a change from liquid to solid state. This process involves a rearrangement of the molecules that align and attach themselves until they form a network that traps the liquid. This network looks like meshes of a net that keep all of the particles in suspension, preventing their aggregation and the collapse of the structure.

Several well-known molecules are able to form gels. The most traditional are found everywhere: flours, tapioca or corn starch, eggs and gelatin. However, non-traditional gelling agents are becoming more commonplace in the market and are widely used in molecular gastronomy: hydrocolloids.

HYDROCOLLOIDS

The use of hydrocolloids in cooking makes it possible to form gels with various textures at temperatures, pH levels and with foods that are impossible to gel with common gelling agents. In addition, the concentration needed to achieve the desired result is often lower, which is a significant advantage that avoids excessive changes in flavor. So it is not surprising to find these texturizing agents in a whole range of consumer products.

The definition of hydrocolloid is not quite established, but the origin of the word greatly helps to understand the meaning. Hydrocolloids become hydrated in water (hence the prefix "hydro"). Once the colloidal solution has formed, it hinders the mobility of water until it becomes thickened or gelled. The long molecules that join together to form a gel through various preparation stages are called polymers. The strength and type of connections determine the characteristics of the gel.

IMPLEMENTATION

As with all culinary techniques, to successfully make a gel using hydrocolloids requires precision and compliance with certain key steps. Considering how easy it is to make instant puddings, this seems a bit excessive, but to guarantee success, there is no room for carelessness!

DISPERSION is an essential step for the formation of a gel and for the thickening of a preparation. An improperly dispersed gelling agent will stick together and form lumps that will alter the subsequent formation of the gel. Dispersion must allow the gelling agent molecules to be completely surrounded by water by separating the powder particles. For several hydrocolloids (agar-agar, carrageenan, sodium alginate, gellan gum), this requires vigorous stirring of the mixture with cold water.

• DISPERSION

Initially, the hydrocolloid particles dispersed in water detach from each other, thus allowing liquid to penetrate into and swell the molecule, and then dissolve.

HYDRATION then allows water to penetrate inside the hydrocolloid molecules, which then facilitate reactions, as it is surrounded by water and suspended in the solvent. This step can be done by gradually heating or chilling the liquid. Agar-agar, carrageenans, some gelatins and gellan gum require heating to hydrate. Alginate hydration requires cooling; the process is described in detail in the section on spherification.

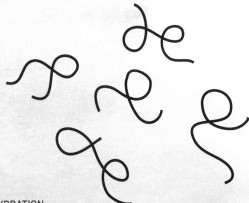

• HYDRATION

Molecules dispersed in the solution are essentially linear polymer chains with few similarities among them at this stage. Once hydrated, the long molecules no longer have any defined structure and are rather randomly organized in the solution.

OTHER CHARACTERISTICS

The gel's final texture varies greatly from one hydrocolloid to another, but several other properties specific to each of the additives can also influence the selection in the development of a recipe.

The strength of bonds between polymer chains influences the gel's texture in the mouth. However, it should also be noted that some hydrocolloids form gels in the presence of ions, such as calcium, magnesium, or potassium. Carrageenans and gellan gum are good examples, making these additives a preferred choice in dairy-based products. Sodium alginate, on the other hand, only reacts in the presence of calcium ions. For more details, read the section on spherification.

The melting point of gels is another characteristic that can be exploited in cooking. A gel obtained from gelatin will melt at a temperature of 99°F (37°C), the same temperature as the human body. Gelatin-based jellies thus create a melt-in-the-mouth sensation. In contrast, agar-agar-based gels have a melting point around

FORMATION of most hydrocolloids occurs after hot hydration, when the temperature drops to a gelling temperature that is specific to each additive. Although some gels are formed before reaching room temperature, others require refrigeration.

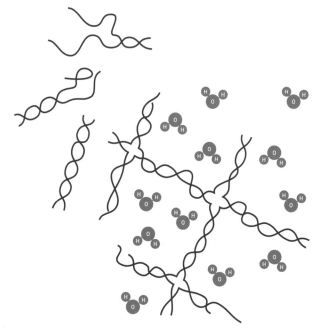

• FORMATION

As the solution cools, the polymer chains twist together and form double helices with other molecules while bonding one molecule to another.

194°F (90°C), which gives these dishes the significant advantage of being able to be served hot.

It should also be mentioned that some hydrocolloids simply have no melting point. The resulting gels are called thermoirreversible, that is, once the bonds between the polymer chains have formed, they cannot be broken. For example, gellan gum-based gels will never melt at temperatures used in cooking and may therefore even be incorporated into stewed dishes!

The gel solution's acidity can also affect the result and therefore some gels do not congeal in the presence of highly acidic ingredients. It is also important to note that the degree of transparency of gels will vary based on the gelling agent chosen. Agar-agar will usually produce cloudy gels, whereas kappa carrageenan and gellan gum will produce gels whose transparency ranges from slightly opaque to opaque. Finally, sodium alginate, gelatin and iota carrageenan produce completely clear gels.

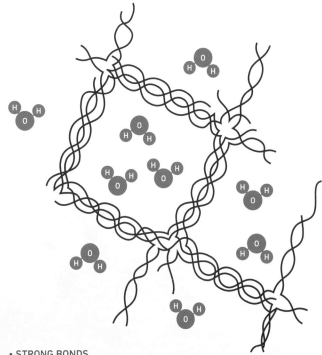

• STRONG BONDS

A strong bond between the molecules is created when multiple links are formed between the double helices. The resulting gel will be firmer and more brittle.

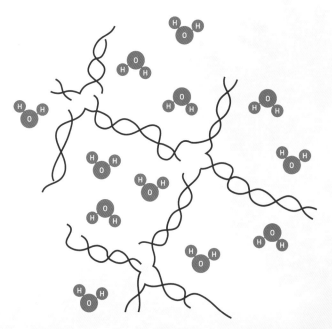

• WEAK BONDS

A weak bond between the molecules will result in softer, more elastic gels.

HYDROCOLLOID SUMMARY TABLE

	AGAR-AGAR	SODIUM ALGINATE	IOTA CARRAGEENAN
Origin	Red algae	Brown algae	Red algae
Clarity	Semi-opaque	Transparent, clear	Semi-opaque
Mouthfeel	Gritty when highly concentrated, soft when lowly concentrated	Soft	Creamy
Texture	Thermoreversible, firm, brittle gel	Thermoirreversible, flexible gel in the presence of calcium, thickener in the absence of calcium	Thermoreversible, flexible gel in the presence of calcium, soft gel in the absence of calcium
Dispersion	In cold or hot water, using a spoon or whisk	In cold water, using a handblender; can be improved by mixing with any powdery ingredient	In cold water, using a handblender; can be improved by mixing with sugar or alcohol
Hydration (activation)	T > 194°F	In cold or hot water	T > 158°F
Setting	Quick (a few minutes); T < 95-113°F	Quick (a few minutes); independently of temperature	Medium (15 minutes); T < 104-158°F
Melting	176-194°F	Does not melt; prolonged heating may destabilize the gel	113-176°F
Prohibitor	Requires prolonged heating with highly acidic or highly basic solutions	Acidic ingredients (pH < 4) and very salty solutions	n/a
Promoter	Sugar	Calcium (essential for gelling)	Calcium
Freezer stable	No	Yes	Yes

KAPPA CARRAGEENAN	COLD SOLUBLE GELATIN	GELLAN GUM (low acyl)
Red algae	Animal protein	Bacterial fermentation
Transparent, clear	Transparent, clear	Transparent
Firm when highly concentrated, soft when lowly concentrated	Soft, melts in the mouth	Firm and brittle
Thermoreversible, brittle gel in the presence of potassium, firm gel in the absence of potassium	Thermoreversible, soft, elastic gel	Thermoirreversible, hard, brittle gel
In cold water, using a handblender; can be improved by mixing with sugar or alcohol	In cold water, using a handblender; can be improved by mixing with any powdery ingredient	In cold water, using a spoon or whisk; can be improved by mixing with sugar or alcohol
T > 158°F	T > 68°F	T > 203°F
Medium (15 minutes); T < 86-140°F	Long (a few hours); T < 59°F	Quick (a few minutes); T < 50-140°F
104-176°F	77-104°F	Does not melt
Salts	Salts, acidic ingredients, solutions with a high alcohol concentration, prolonged heating, kiwi, pineapple, peach, mango	Highly acidic solutions as well as solutions with a high calcium or sodium concentration will prevent hydration
Potassium	Milk, sugar, solutions with a low alcohol concentration	Highly acidic solutions as well as solutions with a high calcium or sodium concentration will promote gelling
No	No	Yes

TIPS & TRICKS
AGAR-AGAR PEARLS

ADDITIVE

Aa

SPECIALIZED TOOLS
- Pipette
- Sieve (or slotted spoon)

Agar-agar can be used to sculpt practically any solution into a gel, be it in the shape of a pearl, a spaghetti or a sheet.

PRINCIPLE

Agar-agar's gelifying properties are activated when the solution is heated to a temperature of 194°F. The gelification process itself is then triggered when the solution cools down to temperatures ranging between 90°F and 110°F. The gel produced will be reversible, so it can be re-melted and re-shaped.

To create pearls, the solution containing agar-agar should be brought to a boil first and then dripped into a cold oil to trigger gelification. So long as the pearls can cool down before they sink to the bottom of the container of oil, they will be perfectly round.

THE SOLUTION TO BE TRANSFORMED

PREPARE APPROXIMATELY ¾ CUP OF A SOLUTION TO BE TRANSFORMED INTO PEARLS.

The acidity of the ingredients used will not impact the gelification process. However, the addition of sugar will strengthen the gel.

WARNING
Denser, thicker solutions such as honey-based or syrup-based solutions can be diluted in order to ensure that they contain enough water to hydrate the agar-agar.

1

PLACE A TALL GLASS OF VEGETABLE OIL IN THE FREEZER, ALLOWING IT TO COOL FOR AT LEAST 30 MINUTES.

N.B. The oil should be cold enough and the glass tall enough for the gelification process to be completed before the drops of the agar-agar solution reach the bottom of the glass.

2

HEAT THE PREPARATION AND SPRINKLE IN ONE SACHET (2G) OF AGAR-AGAR.

N.B. Stir preparation until the agar-agar is completely dissolved.

3

BRING THE PREPARATION TO
A BOIL IN ORDER TO ACTIVATE
THE AGAR-AGAR'S PROPERTIES.

N.B. Remove from stove as soon
as it starts boiling; the preparation
should reach a temperature of
approximately 194°F. Excess boiling
could alter the taste of certain
ingredients.

194°F

4

USING A PIPETTE, DRIP DROPLETS
OF THE AGAR-AGAR PREPARATION
INTO THE COLD OIL.

N.B. The oil shouldn't be too cold or
near-frozen, as this will make the
droplets float. Should this happen,
keep dripping droplets of the hot
preparation into the oil; the droplets
will start sinking as the oil warms up.

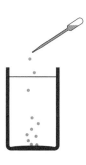

5

COLLECT THE PEARLS USING
A SIEVE AND RINSE THE
PEARLS WITH WATER.

N.B.

Shapeless or flat pearls indicate
that the oil was not cold enough at
the time of dripping the preparation,
or that the glass used wasn't deep
enought.

SERVING AND PRESERVATION

Store the pearls in a closed container in
the fridge for several days if needed. The
pearls can also be left to macerate in the
oil used in previous steps if the taste of
the oil fits with that of the pearls.

Rinsing the pearls with water is optional
if the taste of the oil used in previous
steps fits with that of the pearls. The
same oil could also be used to extend
the pearls' fridgelife.

To serve hot, warm up the pearls by
submerging them in hot water.

TIPS & TRICKS
AGAR-AGAR
SPAGHETTI

Agar-agar can be used to sculpt practically any solution into a gel, be it in the shape of a pearl, a spaghetti or a sheet.

PRINCIPLE

Agar-agar's gelifying properties are activated when the solution is heated to a temperature of 194°F. The gelification process itself is then triggered when the solution cools down to temperatures ranging between 90°F and 110°F. The gel produced will be reversible, so it can be re-melted and re-shaped.

To create spaghetti, the solution containing agar-agar should be brought to a boil, then injected into a silicone tube, then allowed to cool down before being removed.

THE SOLUTION TO BE TRANSFORMED

PREPARE APPROXIMATELY ¾ CUP OF A SOLUTION TO BE TRANSFORMED INTO A SPAGHETTI, AND FILTER IF NEEDED.

The acidity of the ingredients used will not impact the gelification process. However, the addition of sugar will strengthen the gel.

Denser, thicker solutions such as honey-based or syrup-based solutions can be diluted in order to ensure that they contain enough water to hydrate the agar-agar.

WARNING
Small solid particles remaining in a poorly filtered preparation could block the tip of the syringe.

ADDITIVE

Aa

SPECIALIZED TOOLS
- Syringe
- Silicone tubes

1

FILL A TALL CONTAINER WITH COLD WATER AND ICE CUBES.

N.B. Very cold water will accelarate the cooling down of the agar-agar preparation as well as the gelification process.

2

HEAT THE PREPARATION AND SPRINKLE IN ONE SACHET (2G) OF AGAR-AGAR.

N.B. Stir preparation until the agar-agar is completely dissolved.

3

BRING THE PREPARATION TO A BOIL IN ORDER TO ACTIVATE THE AGAR-AGAR'S PROPERTIES.

194°F

N.B. Remove from stove as soon as it starts boiling; the preparation should reach a temperature of approximately 194°F. Excess boiling could alter the taste of certain ingredients.

7

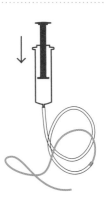

USING A FOOD SYRINGE, INJECT AIR INTO THE TUBE TO EXTRACT THE SPAGHETTI WHILE GRADUALLY INCREASING THE PRESSURE APPLIED ON THE SYRINGE'S PISTON.

4

FILL A FOOD SYRINGE WITH THE PREPARATION AND AFFIX A SILICONE TUBE TO THE SYRINGE.

N.B. Pour the hot agar-agar preparation into a container that will facilitate further manipulations.

N.B.

A spaghetti formed using too little agar-agar will be fragile and will not hold its shape. Should this happen, re-heat the gelified preparation while incorporating more agar-agar, and repeat the previous steps.

A spaghetti formed using too much agar-agar will lack elasticity and will tend to break easily. Should this happen, re-heat the gelified preparation while diluting it, and repeat the previous steps.

5

USING THE SYRINGE, FILL THE SILICONE TUBE WITH THE PREPARATION, WHICH SHOULD STILL BE HOT.

N.B. Small solid particles remaining in a poorly filtered preparation could block the tip of the syringe.

SERVING AND PRESERVATION

Store the spaghetti in a closed container in the fridge for several days if needed.

6

SUBMERGE THE TUBE INTO THE ICED WATER AND LET COOL DOWN FOR 3 MINUTES.

N.B. To be completed, the gelification process requires that the agar-agar preparation cools down completely while in the tube; otherwise, the spaghetti will not hold its shape once it is removed from the tube.

To serve hot, warm up the the spaghetti by submerging them in hot water.

TIPS & TRICKS
AGAR-AGAR
CANNELLONI

Agar-agar can be used to sculpt practically any solution into a gel, be it in the shape of a pearl, a spaghetti or a sheet.

PRINCIPLE

Agar-agar's gelifying properties are activated when the solution is heated to a temperature of 194°F. The gelification process itself is then triggered when the solution cools down to temperatures ranging between 90°F and 110°F. The gel produced will be reversible, so it can be re-melted and re-shaped.

To create cannelloni, the solution containing agar-agar should be brought to a boil, then evenly spread on a smooth surface and allowed to cool down and congeal. The thin sheet of gel thus formed can be rolled up and even stuffed.

THE SOLUTION TO BE TRANSFORMED

PREPARE APPROXIMATELY ¾ CUP OF A SOLUTION TO BE TRANSFORMED INTO A CANNELLONI.

The acidity of the ingredients used will not impact the gelification process. However, the addition of sugar will strengthen the gel.

WARNING
Denser, thicker solutions such as honey-based or syrup-based solutions can be diluted in order to ensure that they contain enough water to hydrate the agar-agar.

1

HEAT THE PREPARATION AND SPRINKLE IN ONE SACHET (2G) OF AGAR-AGAR.

N.B. Stir preparation until the agar-agar is completely dissolved.

2

BRING THE PREPARATION TO A BOIL IN ORDER TO ACTIVATE THE AGAR-AGAR'S PROPERTIES.

N.B. Remove from stove as soon as it starts boiling; the preparation should reach a temperature of approximately 194°F. Excess boiling could alter the taste of certain ingredients.

3

POUR THE PREPARATION
ONTO A PLATE OR A BAKING
SHEET AND TILT IT SO THAT
THE PREPARATION SPREADS
THINLY (1/8 INCH THICK)
AND EVENLY.

4

LET COOL FOR AT LEAST
5 MINUTES.

N.B. To be completed, the
gelification process requires that
the agar-agar preparation cools
down completely; otherwise, the
cannelloni will not hold its shape
during manipulation.

5

USING A KNIFE, CUT THE
GEL INTO RECTANGULAR
PIECES.

6

DEPOSIT A SMALL AMOUNT
OF HOT OR COLD FILLING
ONTO THE SHEET OF GEL TO
CREATE A CANNELLONI.

N.B. Do not put too much filling to
easily fold the cannelloni.

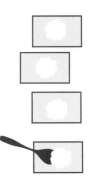

N.B.

An overly thick gel sheet or a gel sheet that
was formed using too much agar-agar
will tend to break when folded. Should this
happen, re-heat the gelified preparation while
diluting it, and repeat the previous steps.

An overly thin gel sheet or a gel sheet that
was formed using too little agar-agar will not
hold its shape when manipulated. Should this
happen, re-heat the gelified preparation while
incorporating more agar-agar, and repeat the
previous steps.

SERVING AND PRESERVATION

Store gel sheets in a closed container in
the fridge for several days if needed.

To serve hot, warm up gel sheets by
submerging them in hot water.

Then place warm filling onto the warm
gel sheet and create the cannelloni.

AGAR-AGAR

Natural gelling agent extracted from red algae often used to create solid pearls, gel spaghettis and jellies.

Although its exotic name may puzzle some consumers, agar-agar has long been known in Japan where consumption and use of algae for culinary purposes goes back centuries. The gelling substance was discovered by accident in 1658. A cook at an inn discarded some left-over gelidium seaweed soup served at dinner. It froze, thawed and dried during adverse weather before finally being found by its creator. He then boiled and cooled the residue and discovered that the resulting jelly had enhanced culinary properties.

It is still possible to find hand-made agar-agar. Although the current manufacturing process still uses the same basic steps (boiling, freezing, thawing, drying), it has however been adapted to modern industrial methods, which obtain a more stable and safer product through effective extraction methods. But the raw material remains the same as when agar-agar was first discovered: Rhodophyceae, red algae, including several genera other than gelidium are now harvested (gracilaria, pterocladia, gellidiella).

In the industry, algae are first washed and then treated with an acid or an alkali to facilitate extraction or to increase the final product's gelling capacity. The plants are then boiled under pressure, filtered and cooled. Next, two methods are used to extract water from the product: either a freezing and thawing process or mechanical pressure is applied to the gel formed upon boiling. Finally, the plant gum obtained is dried and then ground according to the desired form: powder, flakes, bars or threads.

The advantage of this polysaccharide for the food industry and cooking lies in its ability to form a reversible gel which, unlike a gelatin-based gel, requires a low concentration and allows greater flexibility in the temperature at which it can be used. In fact, agar-agar gel only melts at a temperature of around 194°F (90°C) and congeals faster once boiled, as soon as its temperature drops to about 104°F (40°C). When mixed with cold water, agar-agar is insoluble. When it is boiled in water, its polysaccharide linear structure curls and forms helices that then join a more complex arrangement, trapping the water upon cooling.

The result is a brittle, cloudy gel, which allows cooks to sculpt delicious liquid mixtures in many unusual forms such as spaghetti, beads, or thin, tasty sheets that can be rolled.Agar-agar also offers the advantage of not requiring the addition of molecules or other ingredients besides water, since agar-agar molecules bind together due to the hydrogen ions already present in water. In addition, this hydrocolloid can be used with various sugars, proteins and more acidic foods such as fruit. It is worth noting that the addition of large amounts of sugar, up to 60% of the solution, will further strengthen the gel. The use of agar-agar is definitely flexible, but you have to be careful: tannic acid found in squash, apples or plums may hinder the formation of the gel if they are used in large quantities in the gel preparation.

DID YOU KNOW THAT AGAR-AGAR :

Aa	Cl	M	Ic
Agar-Agar	Calcium Lactate	Maltodextrin	Iota Carrageenan
	Ln	Gg	M
	Liquid Nitrogen	Gellan Gum	

Effectively replaces animal gelatin in a vegetarian diet and has virtually no taste or color.

Is used in microbiology as a culture medium for bacteria, cells, yeasts and molds.

Is included in some slimming diets due to its high-fiber, low calorie satiating effect.

Is used as a stabilizer, emulsifier, and gelling and thickening agent in the food processing industry, which accounts for 90% of its total production.

CARRAGEENANS

Natural gelling agent derived from red algae, used to create smooth, elastic gels (iota carrageenan) or firm, brittle gels (kappa carrageenan).

Used for a long time in Ireland, where it is also known as carrageen moss, the inhabitants of this country gave carrageenan its name. As it creates a creamy texture, this dried seaweed was originally boiled with milk to make pudding or thicken infant formula.

Like agar-agar, carrageenan is a hydrocolloid obtained from the cell walls of red algae. As there is a large variety of algae used for extracting the product, their chemical characteristics differ greatly and allow a multitude of uses depending on their origins and composition. Three types of carrageenan stand out depending on the predominance of sugar in their structure: kappa, iota and lambda, which come respectively from Kappachycus alvarezii, Eucheuma denticulatum and Chondrus crispus. Other seaweed is also harvested, including Furcellaria, Gigartina and Iridaea.

The main goal of processing is to isolate the hydrocolloid locked inside the algae. To do this, chemical agents (salts, alcohols, alkalies) and mechanical means, such as filtration, concentration, drying and grinding, are applied to the plant. The salts chosen to extract carrageenan greatly depend on the desired final product and desired gelling properties, since they cause molecular rearrangement. Production of carrageenan requires great precision, in-depth knowledge of its gelling and thickening properties, and standardized procedures in order to create identical mixtures every time and thereby ensure production consistency.

Due to its composition, kappa carrageenan forms a brittle, firm gel, which is potentiated and stabilized by the presence of potassium. Many layers of kappa molecules join together forming double helices that produce this particular texture. The final product is greatly affected by salts, sugar or proteins, such as those present in milk. Interactions between positive and negative charges of the additive and solution create a network similar to the meshes of a net, which keep all of the particles in suspension, preventing their aggregation and the collapse of the structure.

Iota carrageenan has greater affinity with calcium, although it is not necessary in order for it to congeal. Calcium, like potassium with kappa carrageenan, lodges between double helices to stabilize the gel. Iota carrageenan usually produces an elastic gel that does not degrade if it is frozen and thawed. It also forms a stronger gel in the presence of starch.

The third type of carrageenan, lambda, significantly differs from the other two. It does not gel, with or without the addition of ions, but is used to thicken dairy products. It is used less often, but is sometimes combined with kappa to change the texture of certain products.

Finally, it is important to note that acidic foods destroy polysaccharide chains and prevent the product from congealing. It is therefore essential to add this type of ingredient at the very last moment.

DID YOU KNOW THAT CARRAGEENANS:

Ensure the consistency of various dairy products such as cottage cheese and ice cream, as they prevent the separation of proteins.

Keep cocoa particles in suspension in chocolate milk.

Improve the texture of processed products such as sauces, dairy desserts and salad dressings, as they increase the products' viscosity.

Trap moisture in cured meats to give them a juicy texture.

GELLAN GUM

Gelling agent obtained via fermentation used to produce firm gels that slice cleanly and withstand high temperatures.

Gellan gum is a polysaccharide whose origin differs from that of other hydrocolloids presented so far. Its rather recent discovery was the result of industrial research on gum from bacterial fermentation. Sphingomonas elodea bacteria transform simple sugars, phosphate, nitrogen and nutrients into chains of more complex sugars. Once the process has been completed, the microorganisms are eliminated by pasteurization.

Precipitation in alcohol and acyl group clarification or elimination processes are applied to the gum to further transform it. Four derivatives are manufactured in the industry, each with different properties. Two forms are more widely used in cooking: high-acyl and low-acyl gellan gum.

HIGH-ACYL GELLAN GUM

High-acyl gellan gum produces a supple, elastic texture, which is the result of the well-known acyl groups, allowing the formation of helices that trap water. Upon hydration, the gum is insensitive to the presence of calcium or sodium ions, which do not significantly affect the formation of a gel. However, heat is necessary to properly hydrate the molecule, whereas the presence of sugars or acids in excessive quantity can interfere with this crucial step. The gel melts and re-sets at about 158°F to 176°F (70°C to 80°C).

LOW-ACYL GELLAN GUM

Low-acyl gellan gum is more commonly used in molecular gastronomy to make firm, brittle gels that tolerate temperatures up to 284°F (140°C). For this reason, it is preferred in the preparation of hot dishes. However, it must be handled with great care, as it is significantly more sensitive to the presence of ions than its high-acyl counterpart. Hard water, as well as the presence of sugar or an acid solution medium, slows down the hydration process, which requires a higher temperature.

The best way to properly hydrate this product is to mix it with demineralized water or milk, or use sequestering agents and mix vigorously. The sequestering agents used are salts (sodium citrate, sodium hexametaphosphate) which, when dissolved in water, attach to the ions, making them unavailable for the gum in the solution and thus allowing it to hydrate at a lower temperature. The gel forms upon cooling due to the ions present in the food added to the mixture, or by the addition of other ions such as calcium, sodium, magnesium or potassium salts. There are a great variety of solutions with which low-acyl gellan gum can form gels, which greatly increases its possible uses.

DID YOU KNOW THAT GELLAN GUM:

> Replaces agar-agar in culture media that must be maintained at very high temperatures.

Is used in gelatinous beverages that are popular in Asia, but marketing abroad proved to be difficult, particularly in North America with the beverage "Orbitz."

> Adheres salt crystals that are sprayed onto pretzels, without adding fat.

Often replaces pectin in sugar-free jams and is added to dry cake mixes to maintain enough moisture during cooking.

GELATIN

Cold soluble gelatin that has the same textural properties and melt-in-the mouth effect as traditional gelatin.

G

Gelatin is probably one of the best known additives outside the food industry. Its discovery dates back to the Egyptians, who used it to make glue. Since then, its use has obviously become greatly diversified!

Gelatin is naturally formed when meat, bones or skin are slowly boiled to make a stock or stew. Once cooled, the mixture forms a jelly. Gelatin was known and used in cooking well before the product was marketed at the end of the 19th century, when an American named Charles Knox introduced it on the U.S. market in the form of a powder.

Unlike other additives presented in this book, gelatin is of animal origin. Its structure is therefore a blend of amino acids, the components of proteins. Gelatin is derived from collagen found in the skin and bones of beef, pork, fish or poultry. Once these parts are ground, an acid or alkaline treatment is applied to them for days, or even months, after which they are boiled and cleared of impurities through filtration. A concentration of the solution and a high temperature treatment are applied before cooling and drying. On the market, gelatin comes in powder form, flakes, sheets or granules. The origin of the raw material and the processing obviously affect the gel's final strength.

During cooling, chains of amino acids form helices that trap water in a structure resembling a fishing net. Due to gelatin's properties, it can be added to food as a gelling agent, stabilizer, emulsifier and crystal inhibitor. The gel formed is thermoreversible and melts at about body temperature, which creates a melt-in-the-mouth sensation.

The main criticism of gelatin concerns its animal origin and the fear that it may contain contaminants or unwanted bacteria. However, gelatin purity regulations are very strict and only animals that are tested and approved for human consumption are used in the product. In the industry, gelatin is considered an ingredient rather than an additive and no consumption limits have been set.

DID YOU KNOW THAT GELATIN:

| Cl | M | Io |
| Calcium Lactate | Maltodextrin | Iota Carrageenan |

| Kc | G | Ln | Gg | Mc |
| Kappa Carrageenan | Gelatin | Liquid Nitrogen | Gellan Gum | Methylcellulose |

Lends its name to the colored film used on light projectors, as colored gelatin-based gels originally served the same purpose in the first lighting equipment.

Is one of the main components in gel capsules that protect drugs and affect their absorption rate.

Is found in some cosmetics, as one of its derivatives, "hydrolyzed collagen," is known for its anti-aging effects.

Is used to hold silver halide crystals in an emulsion in photographic films.

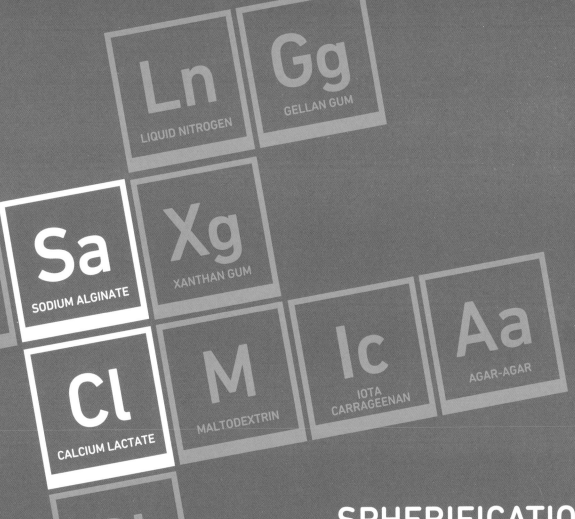

Ln
LIQUID NITROGEN

Gg
GELLAN GUM

Sa
SODIUM ALGINATE

Xg
XANTHAN GUM

Cl
CALCIUM LACTATE

M
MALTODEXTRIN

Ic
IOTA CARRAGEENAN

Aa
AGAR-AGAR

Sl
SOY LECITHIN

SPHERIFICATION

Definition and technique

SPHERIFICATION

So-called spherification is based on a food re-engineering manufacturing process. For years, the food industry has been using this process to re-engineer fruit, vegetable or meat purees into pieces whose form and texture are very similar to the basic ingredient. For example, what appears to be a piece of bell pepper stuffed into pitted olives is actually a gelled and remolded puree. By doing so, the industry is able to maintain consistent uniformity in the appearance of products. In addition, by using puree rather than whole foods, the industry can achieve substantial cost savings.

One thing is for certain: when Catalan chef Ferran Adrià of the famous restaurant El Bulli in Spain adopted and perfected this technique, he had something else in mind other than recycling raw material! In molecular gastronomy, spherification is now defined as the encapsulation of a liquid inside different sized spheres that burst in the mouth.

The wall trapping the liquid inside the sphere consists of a gel formed by a process similar in some respects to the one described in the preceding section on gelling. The additive used is sodium alginate, and just like in the gelling process using carrageenans or gellan gum, the presence of ions is essential for the formation of the gel. In the case of a sodium alginate gel, the presence of calcium ions is required so that the long alginate molecules can align and bind to finally form a gel. To better understand the ability of sodium alginate to form a gel, let's take a closer look at the molecule.

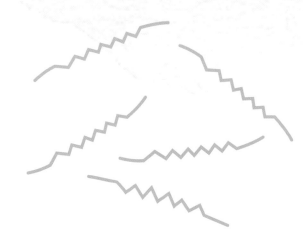

• SODIUM ALGINATE MOLECULE
Sodium alginate is made up of long molecules that look like zigzags.

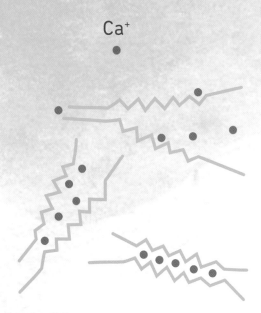

Ca⁺

• CALCIUM IONS REACTION

The long molecule threads are attracted to each other by calcium ions and create a structure that resembles a box of eggs.

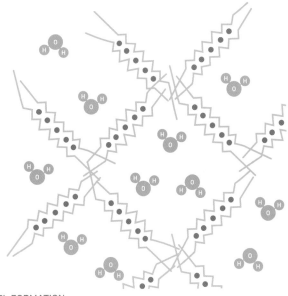

• GEL FORMATION

This process involves a rearrangement of the molecules that align and attach themselves until they form a network that traps the liquid. This network looks like meshes of a net that keep all of the particles in suspension, preventing their aggregation and the collapse of the structure.

Alginate reacts with any calcium that naturally occurs or that has been added to the ingredient to be spherified. For example, we could make a pudding by simply adding sodium alginate to a preparation of milk and sugar, as milk is naturally rich in calcium. Applying this principle, we can precisely control the moment when the calcium and alginate come into contact and thereby diversify the liquids to be gelled and the forms obtained.

Depending on the source of calcium ions, two types of spherification can be used:

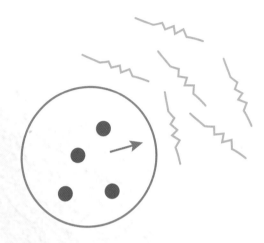

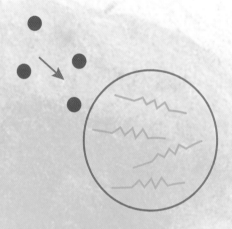

• REVERSE SPHERIFICATION

A solution containing calcium is immersed in a high-sodium alginate bath. Calcium ions migrate from the sphere's interior to its exterior, thus forming a gel wall.

Both techniques can be used to create different sized spheres. However, basic spherification is preferred to create small balls, or caviar, whereas reverse spherification is the preferred method to form larger spheres, also called flavor bubbles.

BASIC
SPHERIFICATION

Basic spherification consists in immersing a liquid containing sodium alginate in a high-calcium bath. Calcium ions then migrate from the sphere's exterior to its interior.

As a large amount of calcium ions remains present in the caviar's wall, even a water rinse will not completely slow down the gelling of the wall, which will thicken until the sphere's interior is completely gelled. Since an in-the-mouth flavor burst is usually desired, it is recommended to serve the caviar as quickly as possible after its formation.

It is important to note that the addition of the sodium alginate solution to the preparation to be transformed significantly dilutes it. So, for maximum flavor, be sure to transform solutions that are highly

• BASIC SPHERIFICATION

A solution containing sodium alginate is poured into a high-calcium bath. Calcium ions migrate towards the solution to be spherified and then trigger the membrane's gelification.

flavorful; otherwise the taste will be rather bland. Sodium alginate will also thicken the preparation. Since the preparation is thicker and less intense in flavor, basic spherification is not recommended for creating large flavor bubbles. However, it is the most practical technique to create small beads, commonly known as flavor caviar.

REVERSE
SPHERIFICATION

As its name suggests, compared with basic spherification, reverse spherification involves a permutation in the process of immersing sodium alginate and calcium salt. The principle is to pour a high-calcium solution in a bath in which sodium alginate has been dissolved. Calcium ions then migrate from the sphere's interior to its wall.

Unlike what happens in basic spherification, it is possible to slow down the wall's thickening process, since rinsing removes excess sodium alginate on the sphere's contours. In the absence of alginate molecules, calcium ions have no effect and the sphere's interior remains liquid. Once rinsed, flavor bubbles can be stored and served sometime after their formation.

Dissolving sodium alginate in a solution significantly thickens it. The sodium alginate bath is therefore very thick and some solutions that are too watery simply cannot penetrate it: the result will look more like a deformed lump of gel than a sphere!

When choosing preparations to be spherified, it is best to work with liquid bases that are naturally thick and high in calcium such as cream, yogurt and certain purees. It is also possible to thicken the preparation to be transformed using a thickening agent such as xanthan gum to minimize the density gap with the sodium alginate bath. However, to spherify very watery solutions, frozen reverse spherification is recommended.

FROZEN REVERSE
SPHERIFICATION

Freezing solutions enables greater precision in the final form and overcomes many of the limitations and constraints of spherification. The technique is straightforward and very similar to reverse spherification.

A pinch of calcium salt is first added to the preparation to be transformed, after which the preparation is molded and frozen. The ice cubes thus produced are then immersed in a sodium alginate bath and rinsed. You no longer have to worry about the preparation's texture, since the ice cubes easily penetrate the surface of the sodium alginate bath. So you can transform completely liquid solutions for an even more spectacular in-the-mouth effect!

OTHER
CHARACTERISTICS

Sodium alginate-based gels are irreversible and therefore can be served hot. To do this, simply immerse the spheres in hot water and wait until the heat is absorbed. In addition, they are resistant to freezing and thawing. The fact that they can congeal cold without prior heating is also a certain advantage.

Nevertheless, it is important to note that the spherification process may be hindered by a high level of acidity or alcohol. Frozen reverse spherification avoids most of these contraindications, obviously provided that the preparation can be frozen.

Finally, be wary of unknown calcium sources that could congeal the preparation without warning. If the tap water is particularly high in calcium, it would be preferable to use bottled water. Also, do not pour the alginate bath down a narrow pipe; otherwise, it could form a blockage!

BASIC
SPHERIFICATION

ADDITIVES

| Cl | Sa |

SPECIALIZED TOOLS
- Pipette
- Sieve (or slotted spoon)

Basic spherification is ideal to create caviars that will liberate their flavors while bursting in your mouth!

For larger spheres, it is recommended to use reverse spherification or reverse frozen spherification.

PRINCIPLE

When a solution containing sodium alginate is dripped into a calcium lactate bath, calcium ions react with alginate molecules by allowing them to align and bind so that a thin gel membrane forms around the droplets. The gelification process that forms the membrane will stop the moment the sphere is rinsed, as its interior will be free of alginate molecules.

THE SOLUTION TO BE TRANSFORMED

PREPARE ABOUT 2 CUPS OF A SOLUTION TO BE SPHERIFIED.

The ingredient chosen must be very tasty, as the solution will lose some of its flavor when the sodium alginate is incorporated to it. An ingredient with high acidity will prevent the spherification process from being completed.

WARNING
Any percentage of calcium in the ingredient will prevent the spherification process from being completed. The use of demineralized water is recommended, as tap water with a high calcium percentage could cause the sodium alginate solution to gelify.

1

DISSOLVE ONE SACHET (2 G) OF SODIUM ALGINATE INTO 2 CUPS OF THE LIQUID INGREDIENT.

N.B. The use of a hand blender is recommended as some egg beaters will not be powerful enough.

2

LET THE PREPARATION SIT FOR AT LEAST 15 MINUTES IN ORDER TO ALLOW THE AIR BUBBLES TRAPPED WITHIN THE SOLUTION FOLLOWING THE BREWING OF THE PREPARATION TO ESCAPE.

N.B. Too many air bubbles will cause the preparation to float when dripped into the calcium lactate bath.

6

RINSE THE CAVIAR
IN COLD WATER.

N.B. Rinsing the caviar is recommended as some calcium molecules may remain attached to it, which can cause the caviar to have a bitter aftertaste. The gelification process as well as the thickening of the caviar's membrane will continue after rinsing.

3

PREPARE A CALCIUM LACTATE BATH BY DISSOLVING ONE SACHET (5 G) OF CALCIUM LACTATE INTO 4 CUPS OF WATER.

N.B.

The interior of a caviar that is being exposed to calcium ions for too long will eventually end up completely congealed.

On the other hand, too short an exposition to calcium ions will cause the caviar's membrane to be too fragile and ultimately unable to maintain its shape.

4

USING A PIPETTE, DRIP DROPLETS OF THE PREPARATION CONTAINING ALGINATE MOLECULES INTO THE CALCIUM LACTATE BATH.

N.B. Hold the pipette horizontally, from a height of approximately 1 inch, and drip slowly and constantly until the pipette is emptied.

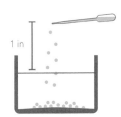

1 in

SERVING AND PRESERVATION

FOR AN OPTIMAL BURST-IN-THE-MOUTH EFFECT, SERVE WITHIN 15 MINUTES.

Store the caviar in its original solution for a maximum of 12 hours before serving. The caviar will be completely congealed, but it should remain very tasty!

The caviar can also be left to macerate in any other tasty solution **to change its taste and color**.

5

QUICKLY COLLECT THE CAVIAR FROM THE CALCIUM LACTATE BATH USING A SIEVE.

N.B. Leaving the caviar to sit in the calcium lactate bath for more than 2 minutes will cause its membrane to thicken until the caviar is completely congealed.

TIPS & TRICKS
REVERSE SPHERIFICATION

SPECIALIZED TOOLS
- Slotted spoon
- Measuring spoon
- Flat-bottom bowl

Reverse spherification is ideal to encapsulate denser, thicker liquids into a sphere that will burst in your mouth!

It is mainly used to spherify purees and dairy products such as yogurts and creams. The frozen version of this technique is recommended for a more liquid sphere interior.

PRINCIPLE

When a solution containing calcium lactate is submerged into a sodium alginate bath, calcium ions react with alginate molecules by allowing them to align and bind so that a thin gel membrane encapsulates the solution. The gelification process that forms the membrane will stop the moment the sphere is rinsed, as its interior will be free of alginate molecules.

THE SOLUTION TO BE TRANSFORMED

PREPARE ABOUT 1 CUP OF A SOLUTION TO BE SPHERIFIED.

The ingredient chosen must be quite dense. Fruit purees, creams and yogurts are recommended as they are very dense; thinner solutions will not penetrate the surface of the sodium alginate bath.

WARNING
The use of demineralized water is recommended, as tap water with a high calcium percentage could cause the sodium alginate bath to gelify.

1

PREPARE THE SOLUTION TO BE SPHERIFIED SO THAT IT HAS A TEXTURE SIMILAR TO THAT OF A DRINKABLE YOGURT.

N.B. Overly thick ingredients can be diluted with milk or water.

2

DISSOLVE A PINCH OF CALCIUM LACTATE INTO THE SOLUTION TO BE SPHERIFIED.

N.B. Pre-dissolve calcium salts in a small quantity of hot water.

3

PREPARE A SODIUM ALGINATE BATH IN A FLAT-BOTTOMED CONTAINER BY DISSOLVING ONE SACHET (2 G) OF SODIUM ALGINATE INTO 2 CUPS OF WATER.

N.B. The use of a hand blender is recommended as some egg beaters will not be powerful enough.

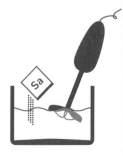

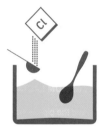

7

COLLECT THE SPHERES
FROM THE SODIUM
ALGINATE BATH USING A
SLOTTED SPOON AND RINSE
THEM IN COLD WATER.

N.B. The gelification process will
stop the moment the spheres
are rinsed, as this will stop the
formation of the membrane.

4

LET THE SODIUM ALGINATE BATH
SIT FOR AT LEAST 15 MINUTES
TO ALLOW THE AIR BUBBLES
TRAPPED WITHIN THE SOLUTION
FOLLOWING THE BREWING TO
ESCAPE.

N.B. Too many air bubbles will prevent
the calcium ions contained within the
frozen spheres from piercing through
the surface of the sodium alginate bath.

N.B.

Should the spheres' membrane
break when manipulated, let the
spheres rest for a longer time in
the alginate bath in order to allow
the membrane to gradually thicken.

5

USING A MEASURING SPOON,
SUBMERGE THE PREPARATION
CONTAINING CALCIUM IONS INTO
THE SODIUM ALGINATE BATH.

N.B. Bring the spoon close to the
sodium alginate bath's surface then,
gradually pour its contents into the bath.
WARNING : Ensure that the spheres do not
touch one another while in the bath,
as this can cause their membranes to
stick together and eventually break.

SERVING AND PRESERVATION

Store the spheres in their original
solution for a maximum of 12 hours
before serving.

To serve hot, let the spheres sit in
hot water before serving.

6

LET THE CALCIUM IONS
AND ALGINATE MOLECULES
INTERACT FOR AT LEAST
3 MINUTES.

N.B. Delicately tilt the spheres in
the sodium alginate bath in order to
ensure that their membrane forms
evenly

Spheres can also be left to macerate in
any other tasty solution **to change the
taste and color** of their gel membrane.

TIPS & TRICKS
REVERSE FROZEN SPHERIFICATION

ADDITIVES

SPECIALIZED TOOLS
- Slotted spoon
- Silicone mold
- Flat-bottom bowl

Reverse frozen spherification is ideal to encapsulate a wide range of liquids into a sphere that will burst in your mouth!

It stands out mainly because of its great versatility, as it allows you to spherify clear liquids such as alcohols and acidic juices such as lemon juice.

PRINCIPLE

When a solution containing calcium lactate is submerged into a sodium alginate bath, calcium ions react with alginate molecules by allowing them to align and bind so that a thin gel membrane encapsulates the solution. The gelification process that forms the membrane will stop the moment the sphere is rinsed, as its interior will be free of alginate molecules.

THE SOLUTION TO BE TRANSFORMED

PREPARE ABOUT 1 CUP OF A SOLUTION TO BE SPHERIFIED.

Toppings such as small pieces of fruit or aromatic herbs can be placed in the mold before freezing in order to remain encapsulated within the spheres.

The use of demineralized water is recommended, as tap water with a high calcium percentage could cause the sodium alginate bath to gelify.

WARNING
Solutions with a high alcohol percentage cannot be frozen in a standard kitchen freezer, and neither can denser, thicker solutions such as honey-based or syrup-based solutions.

1

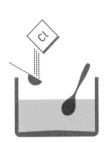

DISSOLVE A PINCH OF CALCIUM LACTATE INTO THE SOLUTION TO BE SPHERIFIED.

N.B. If said solution is of the denser, thicker variety, pre-dissolve calcium lactate into a small quantity of water.

2

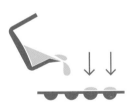

POUR THE PREPARATION INTO A MOLD AND PLACE IT IN THE FREEZER UNTIL COMPLETELY FROZEN.

N.B. Each ice cube will form a sphere. Toppings such as small pieces of fruit or aromatic herbs can be placed in the mold before freezing.

3

PREPARE A SODIUM ALGINATE BATH IN A FLAT-BOTTOMED CONTAINER BY DISSOLVING ONE SACHET (2 G) OF SODIUM ALGINATE INTO 2 CUPS OF WATER.

N.B. The use of a hand blender is recommended as some egg beaters will not be powerful enough.

7

COLLECT THE SPHERES
FROM THE SODIUM
ALGINATE BATH USING A
SLOTTED SPOON AND RINSE
THEM IN COLD WATER.

N.B. The gelification process will
stop the moment the spheres
are rinsed, as this will stop the
formation of the membrane.

4

LET THE SODIUM ALGINATE BATH
SIT FOR AT LEAST 15 MINUTES
TO ALLOW THE AIR BUBBLES
TRAPPED WITHIN THE SOLUTION
FOLLOWING THE BREWING TO
ESCAPE.

N.B. Too many air bubbles will prevent
the calcium ions contained within the
frozen spheres from piercing through
the surface of the sodium alginate bath.

N.B.

Should the spheres' membrane
break when manipulated, let the
spheres rest for a longer time in
the alginate bath in order to allow
the membrane to gradually thicken.

5

SUBMERGE THE FROZEN
SPHERES CONTAINING
CALCIUM IONS INTO THE
SODIUM ALGINATE BATH.

N.B. Ensure that the spheres do
not touch one another while in
the bath by stirring delicately, as
this can cause their membranes
to stick together and eventually
break.

SERVING AND PRESERVATION

Store the spheres in their original
solution for a maximum of 12 hours
before serving.

To serve hot, let the spheres sit in
hot water before serving.

Spheres can also be left to macerate in
any other tasty solution **to change the
taste and color** of their gel membrane.

6

LET THE CALCIUM IONS
AND ALGINATE MOLECULES
INTERACT FOR AT LEAST
3 MINUTES.

N.B. Delicately turn over the
spheres in the sodium alginate
bath in order to ensure that
their membrane forms evenly.

SODIUM ALGINATE

Natural gelling agent extracted from brown algae often combined with a calcium salt in the process of spherification.

Sa

As you probably guessed, the name of this additive comes from its marine origin. In fact, sodium alginate is extracted from brown algae found on the coasts of the North Atlantic, Asia and South America. Its discovery was made by a chemist named E.C.C. Stanford, who described the molecule for the first time in 1881.

The food industry uses this algae extract in many different processes and, depending on the desired properties, manufacturers prefer several varieties of marine plants (Laminaria hyerborea, Laminaria digitata, Laminaria japonica, Ascophyllum nodosum, Ecklonia maxima).

Alginate is a polysaccharide, or a sugar chain, from the cell wall of algae. First extracted in the form of alginic acid, the product is then neutralized with salts that make it soluble and stable in a water solution. The solution goes through sifting, centrifuging and filtration before being precipitated in alginate salt.

Industry takes advantage of many of sodium alginate's properties. Its resistance to heat makes it an ingredient of choice in bakeries to make cream fillings or fruit jellies, allowing them to keep their shape during cooking. In addition, the thin film created around the gel or cream prevents it from affecting cake moisture. Its thickening effect in aqueous solutions is used to create thicker cheese sauces that adhere better to pasta. Alginate is also used as a stabilizer in ice cream by decreasing the size of crystals and obtaining a smoother texture. It also prevents the separation of emulsions such as salad dressings or mayonnaise. Gels form more easily when alginate is added to products with higher calcium concentrations.

Re-shapes chili pepper powder or pulp that can then be used to stuff olives.

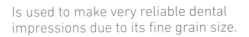 Is used to make very reliable dental impressions due to its fine grain size.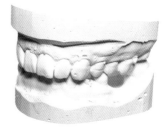

Is used to make replicas of human body parts during filming of special effects.

Encapsulates certain probiotics so that they reach the intestines without being destroyed by stomach acid.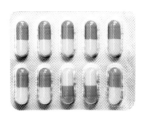

CALCIUM LACTATE

Calcium salt used with sodium alginate in the process of spherification.

A salt is a compound derived from the joining of one positive ion (other than hydrogen H$^+$) with one negative ion (other than hydroxide OH$^-$ ion). Ions can be metals (sodium, potassium), non-metals (carbon), acids (lactic acid) or bases, each providing either a positive or negative ion. Salts are usually very soluble in water.

Table salt, or sodium chloride, is well known for its flavor enhancing and preservative qualities, but in molecular gastronomy, calcium salts are used for gelling with sodium alginate.

Three calcium salts, derivatives of three acids (lactic, gluconic, chloric), are usually used in molecular gastronomy. However, calcium lactate is more popular, since it leaves no aftertaste, whereas calcium chloride leaves a certain bitterness in the mouth, even after rinsing the spheres with water.

The acid part of calcium lactate is derived from lactic acid, an acid available during the fermentation of sugars by lactobacilli bacteria. These same bacteria are needed to make yogurt, cheese and wine. For people with calcium deficiency, calcium lactate is one of the most recommended supplements due to its high absorption rates.

Calcium lactate is found in milk powder, but it is also used as a substrate for yeast in bakery products, an acidity stabilizer in baking powder, and a firming agent for grapefruit and canned peas.

DID YOU KNOW THAT
CALCIUM LACTATE:

Increases the remineralization of enamel when added to chewing gum containing xylitol.

Is found in many aged cheeses, where it is produced by bacteria during the aging process.

Is used as a firming agent for fresh-cut fruits and vegetables as well as processed fish to prevent the degradation of their texture.

Is prescribed to treat calcium deficiency and osteoporosis.

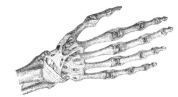

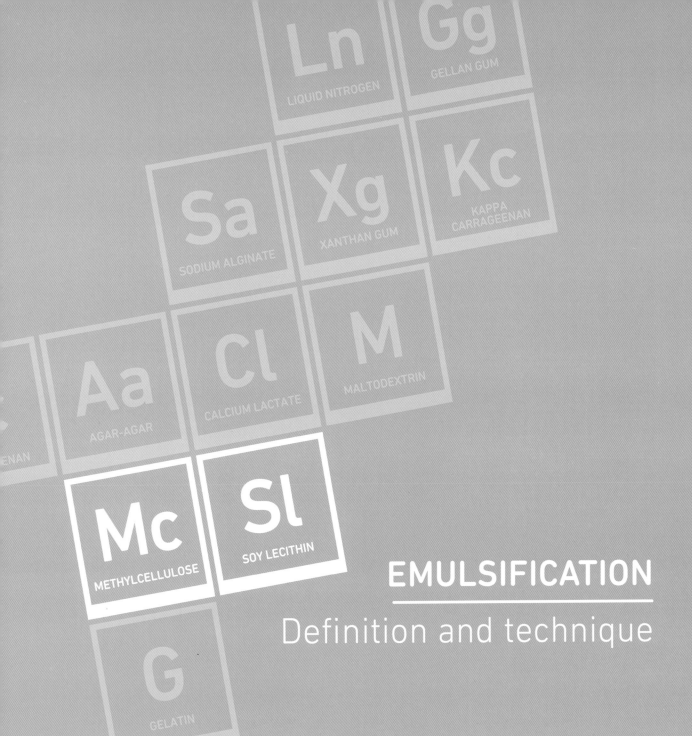

EMULSIFICATION

Definition and technique

EMULSIFICATION

What do chocolate, mayonnaise, salad dressing, milk, butter and ice cream have in common? All of them are emulsions!

The naked eye can only see a homogeneous product. However, this is not the case under the microscope, where thousands of small droplets dispersed in a second liquid substance can be seen. In each case, two substances that are normally immiscible, oil and water, have been mixed using an emulsifying agent.

An emulsion can also present the above-mentioned products in a different way. For example, a liquid can trap air bubbles and turn it into a foam. In molecular gastronomy, emulsification is the technique used to incorporate and stabilize air bubbles in a liquid mixture. It is possible to incorporate air bubble into a liquid simply by whisking vigorously. However, this phase is highly unstable and the air escapes in a relatively short time. To avoid this instability, an emulsifier can be incorporated into the solution.

Egg and milk protein, bread starch, gelatin and cream fat are common emulsifiers that have used in traditional cuisine for a long time. However, in recent decades, the food industry intensified its research in this field and discovered new emulsifiers such as soy lecithin and methylcellulose. These products are also called surfactants, a word derived from "surface active agents," since their molecules act as a barrier (interface) between water and air.

These additives bring great pleasure to molecular gastronomy enthusiasts by reducing the tension between the water and air surface, which stabilizes the air and foam. To better understand the forces at work, let's take a closer look at what happens inside air that is stabilized using soy lecithin.

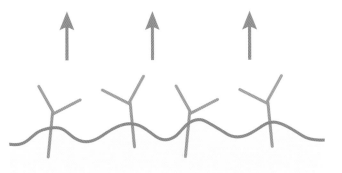

• LECITHIN MOLECULE
The lecithin molecule looks like a hydrophilic pinhead, attracted by water, with two hydrophobic fatty acid legs that are repelled by water.

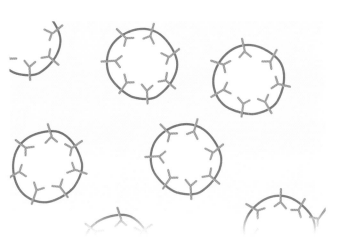

• AIR BUBBLES FORMATION
The lecithin molecule positions itself around air bubbles, which inflate their hydrophilic portion towards the water. The air bubbles' surface is surrounded by lecithin molecules, thus preventing water from escaping from the liquid, which would deflate the foam.

OTHER CHARACTERISTICS

The secret of a successful foam is the amount of air bubbles dispersed in the liquid. In fact, a foam containing a larger number of small air bubbles is generally more stable than one formed using a small number of large bubbles.

So foam made with a whisk does not last as long as one made using a hand blender, since this powerful machine's cuts and re-cuts more air bubbles. A large amount of bubbles dispersed in the liquid also increases the viscosity of solutions, which gives foams their creaminess.

Although their viscosity increases the stability, foam and air remain relatively unstable; air bubbles gradually escape the liquid in which they were incorporated. Three main causes accelerate this phenomenon. First, the air can easily dissolve in liquids and evaporate. Next, the internal pressure of very tiny bubbles increases as their size decreases, eventually causing their membranes to burst. Finally, as there is a significant difference between the density of fluid and air, the two phases tend to separate, and liquid will gradually migrate to the bottom of the dish.

Finally, even when made using translucent ingredients, foams are always opaque. This unusual fact is explained by the many angles of light reflected on the walls of the air bubble. The light that is diffused in all directions thus creates the opacity and a certain brightness, depending on the color of the initial ingredients.

ADDITIVE

Sl

SPECIALIZED TOOLS
- Flat-bottom square bowl
- Hand blender

Soy lecithin is used to transform any liquid into a light and tasty foam.

PRINCIPLE

Soy lecithin is a natural protein contained in soy that has the unique property of stabilizing foam. This emulsifier is used to reach an unusal equilibrium between air and liquid. The foam will stand for about 30 minutes before it begins to dry, however the soy lecithin solution can be re-blended several times in order to obtain more foam.

THE SOLUTION TO BE TRANSFORMED

PREPARE APPROXIMATELY 1⅓ CUPS OF A SOLUTION TO BE LATHERED AND POUR INTO A FLAT-BOTTOMED CONTAINER.

The solution to be spherified must contain a large proportion of water in order to favor the adherence of the lecithin molecules between the water and air bubbles.

WARNING
Denser, thicker solutions such as honey-based or syrup-based solutions should be avoided, as the lecithin molecules do not contain enough water to retain the air bubbles.

1

DISSOLVE ONE SACHET (2 G) OF SOY LECITHIN INTO THE SOLUTION TO BE LATHERED.

N.B. The use of a hand blender is recommended as some egg beaters are not powerful enough.

2

INCORPORATE AS MUCH AIR AS POSSIBLE INTO THE SOY LECITHIN PREPARATION IN ORDER TO PRODUCE FOAM.

N.B. Hold the hand blender at an angle and avoid completely immersing its head.

3

COLLECT FOAM AND SERVE.

N.B. The foam will hold for
approximately 30 minutes before
it starts drying.

4

REBLEND THE SOY
LECITHIN PREPARATION
SEVERAL TIMES IN ORDER
TO OBTAIN MORE FOAM.

SERVING AND PRESERVATION

The foam will hold for approximately
30 minutes before it starts drying.

Store the soy lecithin preparation in a
closed container in the fridge for a few
days if needed. Reblend the soy lecithin
preparation several times in order to
obtain more foam.

SOY LECITHIN

Natural emulsifier extracted from soybean, often used to shape watery solutions into airs.

Sl

Although you may not be aware of the usefulness of the lecithin molecule, your body knows very well how to use it! Lecithin is a constituent of cell membranes, specifically a phospholipid. It is like a hydrophilic pinhead with two hydrophobic fatty acid legs, which are essential properties for the formation of emulsions.

Besides cells in the human body, lecithin is mainly found in egg yolks, soybeans, liver, and wheat germ. The pharmacist Théodore Gobley isolated and described egg lecithin for the first time in 1847. Gobley gave it the name lekithos, the Greek word for egg yolk. He then spotted the group of molecules in many parts of animal bodies and in large quantities in the bile, blood and brain.

Lecithin found in eggs remains the most popular for making mayonnaise or hollandaise sauce, but industry usually extracts it from soy. During the manufacturing process, the soybean is first cooked, then crushed and finally precipitated by alcohol.

Lecithin is found in margarines and infant formula where it acts as an emulsifier. It is also found on the list of ingredients for ice preparations, such as sorbets and ice milk, where it allows fat to remain soluble in a high-water compound.

The body has the ability to manufacture lecithin, but if you want to use this product as a supplement, like fats, it provides the equivalent of 9 kilocalories per gram.

DID YOU KNOW THAT
SOY LECITHIN:

Is incorporated into many cosmetics to help soften the skin and better absorb other ingredients.

Is used as a supplement in many types of animal food, providing fat and protein.

Enhances the color and forms a protective coating on painted surfaces when added to paint.

Prevents food from sticking to the bottom of dishes and pans when added to non-stick cooking sprays.

METHYLCELLULOSE

Natural emulsifier derived from cellulose, used to create denser foams and, when exposed to heat, to create gels that will melt as they cool down.

Derived from cellulose, a structural component of plant cells, methylcellulose was first introduced at the end of the 1930s in Germany, then a few years later in the United States. This extract from wood or cotton has several desirable characteristics such as film formation, water retention and the ability to form a gel with heat, which will melt upon cooling. It also acts as a thickening and binding agent.

Extraction of methylcellulose first requires mixing with an alkali, followed by the addition of methyl chloride, which transfers its methyl group to the molecule. The resulting pulp is then rinsed and filtered at a high temperature, so as to avoid gelling the product. Other cellulose by-products are also available on the market, such as hydroxypropyl methylcellulose (HPMC) and super methylcellulose (SMC).

Vegetable gum is soluble in cold water and forms a soft to firm elastic gel at temperatures around 122°F (50°C), although certain classes of the product can form a gel at about 86°F (30°C). When the temperature drops, the gel then returns to its original form as a solution. By heating, the molecule gets rid of its bonds with the water and forms new ones with its own kind, thus creating the structure needed for a gel. However, the addition of salt or sugar decreases the temperature at which the gel forms. The molecule also has hydrophobic characteristics and is able to trap air, which makes it the emulsifier of choice.

Methylcellulose is useful in the industry due to its stability during cooking and its ability to trap moisture and air, which increases the volume of dough and frozen dairy products. When added to French onions, it preserves the onion's shape and texture during cooking and reduces oil absorption by forming a film.

The ability of methylcellulose to preserve the shape of products makes it a popular ingredient in waffles and soy-based imitation meat. The presence of methylcellulose causes the formation of a gel during cooking, preventing the product from disintegrating, since it will be trapped by the gel. Once the food is cooled and the methylcellulose has returned to its soluble form, the gel disappears. No one will be any the wiser!

DID YOU KNOW THAT
METHYLCELLULOSE:

Is calorie-free when ingested, as human digestive enzymes are unable to alter its molecules; the intestine does not retain it.

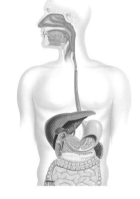

Is used in the composition of anti-constipation treatments due to its ability to absorb a lot of water during its passage through the digestive tract.

Is a main component in the manu-facturing of fake semen used in the pornography industry.

Acts as a performance additive in concrete mixtures due to its properties that improve the product's viscosity and its adhesion to surfaces.

OTHER TRANSFORMATIONS
Definition and technique

OTHER
TRANSFORMATIONS

Chefs who are passionate about molecular gastronomy adore innovating and experimenting. The modern cook's hardware is constantly expanding and culinary techniques are continually improving and being reinvented. Gelling, spherification and emulsification are the flagship techniques in molecular gastronomy. However, many other techniques are also used.

SIPHON
WHIPPING

Siphon whipping differs from emulsification in that foams can be made without using an emulsifying agent. The product resulting from siphon whipping is usually called espuma, derived from the Spanish word for "foam".

The culinary whipper has been used for a long time to make Chantilly cream, also known as whipped cream. To do this, the cream is first poured into the siphon. Then an oxide nitrous (N2O) cartridge is inserted into the device, which releases its gas inside the bottle. Pressurized gas bubbles then penetrate the fatty liquid. This is why the cream's volume increases once the liquid has been ejected from the siphon. It is worth noting that the volume obtained is much greater than that achieved when using a whisk to make whipped cream.

Many espumas are made using liquid ingredients to which cream is added. Creams and other high-fat materials are always beneficial additions to espumas since fat molecules facilitate the dissolving of gas in the preparation. Solid ingredients can also be used, as long as the preparation is filtered before being transformed with the food siphon. Simply transform solid foods by cooking, then pureeing and extracting the juice using a fine sieve. Even very small particles may obstruct or clog the food siphon while it is pressurized.

Finally, emulsifiers or gelling agents can be substituted for cream fat. Additives such as gelatin, agar-agar or xanthan gum can help stabilize any kind of espuma – some may even be served hot! As with all recipes requiring hydrocolloids, we recommend letting the preparation settle a bit while the gas is pressurized in order to allow the molecules to hydrate. A settling period of 20 minutes inside the food siphon yields a much higher volume of an espuma compared with one in which the hydrocolloid does not have the time to properly hydrate.

SUSPENSION
AND THICKENING

Thickening is not a new or spectacular culinary technique, but some thickening agents borrowed from the food processing industry are increasingly used in creative cuisine to add a slight touch of extravagance to dishes and cocktails! Without a doubt, xanthan gum is an additive that is becoming increasingly popular.

Due to its ability to replicate a creamy texture, xanthan gum is often used as a fat replacement in preparations. This creaminess is created by the bonds that join between the gum molecules, which form a network that traps air in the liquid preparation.

This same property is also used in molecular mixology whereby xanthan gum is added to cocktails to create a suspension effect. You can thus "suspend" fruit, herbs or flavor caviar in a liquid.

POWDERIZING

Another technique used in some recipes in this book is the transformation of liquids with high fat content into a fine powder. The additive that makes this technique possible is called maltodextrin and is derived from tapioca sugar, which comes in the form of a very low density powder.

The transformation into powder is a very straightforward process: simply add maltodextrin powder to a high-fat preparation and blend until you get the desired powdery texture. The solid ingredients must first be liquefied and it may be necessary to pass the powder through a sieve to remove any lumps.

So it's easy to add an entirely new dimension to dishes with a powder made from olive oil, chocolate, peanut butter or even bacon! By reducing the proportions of maltodextrin in the mixture, it is also possible to create flavored "lumps" that can be caramelized and crisped on the outside.

DEEP
FREEZING

Liquid nitrogen has long been used in molecular gastronomy demonstrations and the instantaneous vapor cloud that results from the condensation of ambient air is very impressive.

However, besides its "wow" effect, there's another reason for this technique's enduring popularity. Due to its ability to quickly cool preparations, liquid nitrogen significantly outperforms the classic freezing process. Freezing at -4°F (-20°C) causes water to form into increasingly larger crystals and alters the product's initial structure. Frozen products thus lose a lot of their water and soften. The radical change in temperature brought about by nitrogen ensures the formation of much smaller ice crystals that leave the product's cell structure intact.

In cooking, liquid nitrogen is used as a coolant. It is not an ingredient and so it is never ingested; it cools the food, then evaporates. The food can be ingested only after the liquid nitrogen has fully evaporated. Foods that have been cooled with liquid nitrogen are extremely cold, as they have been in contact with this cryogenic substance, and should be left to warm up before being touched and ingested, in the same way that foods dipped in boiling oil must cool down before being touched. The denser the food, the colder it will be and therefore the longer it will need to warm up. This is why chefs usually dip low density confections, such as meringues or frozen mousse, into liquid nitrogen.

Some chefs use the cooling properties of liquid nitrogen to make extremely smooth ice cream. The creaminess of the ice cream is obtained due to the small size of the ice crystals formed during cooling with liquid nitrogen. Liquid nitrogen makes it possible to freeze alcohol to make original cocktails, which is not possible with traditional freezing techniques. It is also possible to create flavor powders using ingredients such as fruit or flowers that have been crushed when frozen.

However, the extreme cold of liquid nitrogen makes handling very dangerous. We recommend that you take training to understand the reactivity and risk of burns.

TIPS & TRICKS
SIPHON
WHIPPING

ADDITIVES

Aa   G   Xg

SPECIALIZED TOOLS
- Sieve
- Culinary whipper
- N2O gas cartridges

There is much more one can do with a culinary whipper than make whipped cream !

PRINCIPLE

A culinary whipper is designed to obtain a foamy mousse from a liquid by injecting gas into a closed flask containing the liquid and expelling it out under pressure. Siphons are available in several volumes (0,25L, 0,5L et 1L) and some can be used for hot preparations as well as cold ones.

Using food additives increases the number of ways a siphon can be used. For instance, xanthan gum can be used to replace the binding effect which is usually provided by the fat of cream to create an incredibly tasty low-fat whipped cream. Further, agar-agar allows the creation of warm mousses that can be served as appetizers or side dishes and cold soluble gelatin adds an exquisite melt-in-the-mouth effect to desserts !

THE SOLUTION TO BE TRANSFORMED

PREPARE ROUGHLY 1½ CUPS OF PREPARATION FOR A 500 ML SIPHON.

The solution to be whipped must contain either a fatty base like full-fat liquid cream, a gelifying base like agar-agar, gelatin, a supportive additive like xanthan gum or egg whites (not beaten). Depending on the doses and the more or less liquid consistency of the preparation poured into the siphon, the result will appear as anything from light and froth-like to solid whipped cream.

WARNING
The siphon can easily become blocked. The preparation must absolutely be filtered through a very fine sieve before being poured into the siphon.

1

PASS THE PREPARATION THROUGH A SIEVE AND FILL THE SIPHON.

N.B. Do not fill the siphon completely (maximum up to 3/4) as there must be enough room for the gas. Only use soluble ingredients. Solid substances such as seeds and pulp will clog the discharging valve.

2

CLOSE THE SIPHON AND INSERT AN N2O GAS CARTRIDGE

N.B. Before loading a cartridge, make sure that the lid is tightly sealed. A light hissing sound indicate that the cartridge has been loaded. Use one cartridge per filling unless otherwise specified in the recipe.

5

TO SERVE, HOLD THE WHIPPER
UPSIDE DOWN VERTICALLY
AND PRESS LEVER SLOWLY
AND PROGRESSIVELY.

N.B. The trigger is very sensitive.
To avoid creating a mess, slowly
press the trigger over the sink to
let out a bit of air pressure.

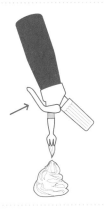

3

HOLD THE WHIPPER
VERTICALLY AND SHAKE
BRISKLY 4 OR 5 TIMES.

N.B. Always shake the siphon
immediately after inserting
the gas cartridge and before
each use.

N.B.

To serve warm espumas made out of agar-agar, mixtures can
be warmed up directly in the culinary whipper by simply soaking
the whipper in a bowl of hot water (158°F/ 70°C) before serving.
Avoid putting a pressurised whipper directly on a hot burner or
in boiling water.

Xanthan gum works like thousands of tiny sponges which is why
it needs some time inside the whipper to hydrate before serving.

Cold soluble gelatin creates best results when used in cold
recipes.

4A

FOR COLD PREPARATIONS,
REFRIGERATE FOR AT
LEAST 30 MINUTES.

N.B. Depending on the recipe,
the siphon must be refrigerated
horizontally for 30 minutes to
2 hours.

SERVING AND PRESERVATION

WARNING
Do not open the whipper before pressure
has completely escaped. Before removing
the head, allow the remaining pressure to
escape by pressing the lever.

To keep its content fresh for several
days, place the whipper in the refrigerator.
To do so, remove the decorative nozzle,
rinse it thoroughly and put it back on.

Thoroughly clean each individual
component with a mild detergent and a
brush. It is particularly important to wash
the head of the siphon to avoid any food
residues to mildew and give a bad taste
to the next preparations. The head is in
general dismountable.

4B

FOR HOT PREPARATIONS,
PLACE IN A HOT WATER BATH.

N.B. Hot preparations can sit in the
hot water bath or be served as soon
as the gas is incorporated into the
preparation. Verify that the siphon
is heat resistant. The hot water bath
must not exceed temperatures of
120°F. Use a thermometer to keep
track of the temperature.

120°F

XANTHAN GUM

Natural thickener derived from glucose via fermentation, often used to stabilize emulsions and thicken sauces and drinks.

Derived from a fermentation process by bacteria, xanthan gum was discovered in the 1950s by American scientists. The microorganism Xanthomonas Campestri transforms sugars, nitrogen, magnesium and other minerals into polysaccharides. This transformation is a little like yeast which, when combined with sugars, produces alcohol and carbon dioxide.

These micro-organisms occur naturally on plants in the cabbage family and they are often responsible for the presence of dark spots on broccoli, cauliflower and other leafy vegetables. In factories, the bacteria are inoculated in a sterile environment until their fermentation has finished. The microorganisms are finally eliminated by heat and the gum is collected through precipitation, centrifuging and drying.

Xanthan gum belongs to the hydrocolloid family, and like each member of this family, its molecules must have time to hydrate after having been dissolved. This hydration period allows water to penetrate inside hydrocolloid molecules, which then facilitate reactions as they are surrounded by water and suspended in the solvent. Hydration can be done equally well in a hot or cold liquid.

Heat only slightly alters the thickening effect of xanthan gum once the product has cooled, but its viscosity is temporarily decreased during the process. This additive also tolerates a wide range of pH and the presence of salts and alcohol up to 60%, but it is best to complete the hydration phase before these additions.

Xanthan gum is a thickener and stabilizer, but it does not form a gel. Rather, it suspends particles in salad dressings and gives sauces their creamy texture. By preventing bread starches from crystallizing, it also preserves freshness. For this reason, it is commonly used in bakeries.

Pseudoplasticity is also a property of xanthan gum widely used by the industry. It consists in the ability of a preparation to change from a thick, viscous form to an almost liquid state after stirring. A dressing containing xanthan gum will thus be thick when the bottle is slowly turned upside down, but its contents become liquid if the bottle is vigorously shaken before being turned upside down. It returns to its original viscosity when put back to rest.

Fifty percent of xanthan gum is used outside the food industry, including cosmetics, personal hygiene products, and the pharmaceutical industry, where it is also used as a stabilizer.

DID YOU KNOW THAT
XANTHAN GUM:

 Causes a noticeable increase in viscosity at concentrations as low as 1%.

Prevents the formation of ice crystals in ice cream and increases the moisture and volume of gluten-free bakery products.

 Provides a high fat mouth feel in many light sauces, milk shakes and dips.

Is a common ingredient in fake blood recipes.

MALTODEXTRIN

Unsweet sugar mostly used in creative cooking as an aroma carrier, in the form of tasty powder that can be sprinkled over food preparations and dishes.

Maltodextrin is derived from starch from grains such as corn or rice, tubers such as potatoes, or roots such as tapioca. This starch is composed of long chains of sugar and is the plant's food reserve.

Once the starch is extracted from the original product, it is hydrolyzed, that is, degraded by enzymes. The process is virtually the same as in starch degradation by enzymes in the digestive system.

Although the composition of maltodextrin is a blend of sugar, its sweetening power is much weaker than that of syrups and table sugar! The indicator used to measure the hydrolysis degree of sugars is called "Dextrose Equivalent" (DE). DE ranges from 0 to 100 where 0 corresponds to untransformed starch and 100 corresponds to simple dextrose molecules, i.e., entirely hydrolyzed sugar. On this scale, refined sugar of the type generally used in cooking occupies the 92 to 99 range. Syrups, such as corn syrup, have a DE between 20 and 91. Maltodextrins have a DE below 20, so they range between starch and syrups.

In the food industry, maltodextrin is used to make soft, low-fat bakery products. It also prevents the formation of crystals on the surface of frozen foods and is used as a sugar substrate in sports drinks.

Besides the food sector, its uses are diverse. Some soaps use it as an aroma carrier and texturizer. The pharmaceutical industry uses its properties to reduce crystallization in syrups and as a filler in tablets.

The use of maltodextrin has been further extended in molecular gastronomy by absorbing fats to create flavorful powder. Since maltodextrin is easily soluble in water – and therefore in the saliva – once in the mouth, these powders melt and release their fat.

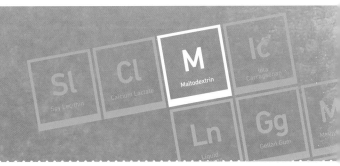
Is added to beer to improve its mouthfeel.

Is a significant part of the content of powdered energy drinks used by athletes.

Is used in the manufacturing of many drugs to improve taste, shape or solubility.

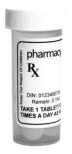

Is considered by nutritionists to be an empty substance containing virtually no calories, vitamins or nutrients.

LIQUID NITROGEN

A major component of air used in its liquid form to create the smoothest ice cream and cook with the cold.

It was not until the 19th century that scientists managed to liquefy gases by cooling them to extreme temperatures.

Nowadays, the usefulness of such processes is undeniable, and it is now impossible to visit a hospital without coming face-to-face with a liquid oxygen tank. Liquid nitrogen is also widely used in this environment to conserve body fluids such as blood or sperm, in addition to eliminating potentially malignant skin lesions such as warts.

Chef Heston Blumenthal introduced liquid nitrogen to the world of molecular gastronomy through Peter Barham, a physics professor and author of the book "The Science of Cooking." In the early 2000s, the chef of the restaurant "Fat Duck" in the United Kingdom served a foam cryogenized with liquid nitrogen from start to finish in front of his clients.

One must always exercise great caution when handling liquid nitrogen. The gas maintained in a liquid state at a temperature of -321°F (-196°C) tries to escape and evaporate. It must be carefully carried in containers provided for this purpose, such as Dewar flasks, double-wall insulated vessels designed for liquefied gases. Keeping liquid nitrogen in an airtight container would turn it into a real pressure bomb! Liquid nitrogen can also cause serious cold burns. In addition, if it is used in a poorly ventilated room, it can cause asphyxiation. The expression "handle with care" therefore makes sense!

DID YOU KNOW THAT LIQUID NITROGEN:

7

N

2
5

Nitrogen

14.007

Is produced directly from ambient air liquefied after distillation separates its various components.

Has been used since 1902 as a source of energy to propel a cryogenic motor vehicle.

Is the basis for a new concept in ecological funerals whereby the corpse is dipped in liquid nitrogen and then turned into fine particles.

Is used to cool certain materials to produce a state of superconductivity.

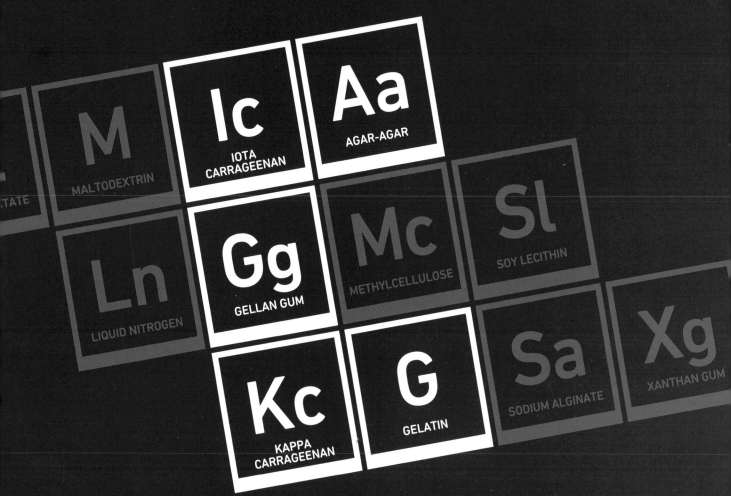

GELIFICATION
___
Recipes

CHOCOLATE FLAN AND PEANUT POWDER

INGREDIENTS

CHOCOLATE PUDDING

Dark chocolate	2 oz (60 g)
Water	¾ cup (180 ml)
35% cooking cream	½ cup (120 ml)
Sugar	0.5 oz (15 g)

PEANUT BUTTER POWDER

Peanut Butter	0.2 oz (5 g)

ADDITIVES

IOTA CARRAGEENAN	1 g (0.05 oz)
TAPIOCA MALTODEXTRIN	5 g (0.2 oz)

DIFFICULTY	🍴
PREP TIME	10 MIN
REST TIME	15 MIN

ADDITIVES | Ic | M |

TOOL

DIRECTIONS

CHOCOLATE PUDDING

1. Melt the chocolate in the microwave, then pour it into a saucepan with all the other ingredients and the **IOTA CARRAGEENAN**.

2. Heat the preparation on a stove while mixing it all together with a hand blender. As soon as it starts to boil, remove it from the stove.

3. Pour the mixture into silicone rectangular molds and place in the fridge for 15 minutes or until it is completely congealed.

PEANUT BUTTER POWDER

1. Using a fork, mix the peanut butter and **TAPIOCA MALTODEXTRIN** together until a powder is obtained.

SERVING SUGGESTION

Carefully unmold the chocolate pudding. Sprinkle the peanut butter powder over the chocolate pudding.

GELIFICATION : CARRAGEENAN PUDDING

Add the **IOTA CARRAGEENAN** to the warm preparation and mix while heating

Pour into rectangular molds and refrigerate for 15 minutes

MALTODEXTRIN POWDER

Gradually add **TAPIOCA MALTODEXTRIN** while mixing with a fork until the desired texture of powder is obtained

DECONSTRUCTED CLAM RISOTTO

INGREDIENTS

CLAM-FLAVORED RICE

Canned clam juice	¾ cup (180 ml)
Soy sauce	¼ cup (60 ml)
Ice cubes	20
Cold water	1 large bowl

CLAM SAUCE

Butter	1 oz (30 g)
Shallot, chopped	1
Garlic	½ clove
White wine	¼ cup (60 ml)
Canned clams with juice	1 cup (235 ml)
35% cooking cream	½ cup (120 ml)
Salt	to taste
Pepper	to taste

ADDITIVE

AGAR-AGAR	2 g (1 sachet)

DIFFICULTY	🍳
PREP TIME	30 MINUTES
REST TIME	10 MINUTES
ADDITIVE	Aa
TOOLS	
TIPS & TRICKS	P. 20

DIRECTIONS

CLAM-FLAVORED RICE

1. Bring the canned clam juice, soy sauce and the **AGAR-AGAR** to a boil and stir for 2 minutes.

2. Place the ice cubes in a large bowl, then fill with cold water.

3. Using the syringe, siphon off some of the clam juice preparation and inject it into the silicone tubes.

4. Immerse the silicone tubes in cold water for 4 minutes.

5. Use the syringe to inject air into the silicone tubes and eject the spaghetti.

6. Repeat steps 3 to 5 until enough gel spaghettis are made. Refrigerate.

CLAM SAUCE

1. Melt the butter in a pan and brown the shallot and garlic.

2. Deglaze the shallot and garlic with white wine and reduce.

3. Add the clam juice from the canned clams to the pan, and bring to a boil.

4. Add the clams and cream. Season with salt and pepper and cook for 2 minutes.

SERVING SUGGESTION

Chop the spaghettis slantwise into rice-shaped pieces. Serve the clam-flavored rice on a plate coated with clam sauce.

GELIFICATION: AGAR-AGAR SPAGHETTIS

Add AGAR-AGAR to the preparation and bring to a boil

Using a syringe, fill a silicone tube with the preparation

Cool down

Eject the spaghetti from the silicone tube

EDIBLE MARGARITA

INGREDIENTS

White tequila	½ cup (120 ml)
Grand Marnier	¼ cup (60 ml)
Lime juice	¼ cup (60 ml)
Edible flowers	to taste

ADDITIVE

COLD SOLUBLE GELATIN	4 g (1 sachet)

DIRECTIONS

1. In a bowl, mix all ingredients together with the **COLD SOLUBLE GELATIN** using a hand blender until smooth.

2. Pour the preparation into a half spherical mold and refrigerate for 3 hours or until it is completely congealed.

3. Unmold the spheres and serve.

SERVING SUGGESTION

Decorate the spherical margaritas with a few edible flower petals.

GELIFICATION

Add the **COLD SOLUBLE GELATIN** to the preparation and pour into half-spherical silicone molds

Unmold when completely congealed

Serve

SALAD AND RASPBERRY FLAKES

INGREDIENTS

RASPBERRY FLAKES

Raspberry vinegar	⅜ cup (100 ml)
Sugar	0.7 oz (20 g)

DRESSING

Goat's cheese, crumbled	to taste
Raspberry vinegar	1⅓ tbsp (20 ml)
Olive oil	2 tbsp (30 ml)
Salt	to taste
Pepper	to taste
Baby arugula shoots	to taste
Pecans, slivered	to taste

ADDITIVE

GELLAN GUM	5 g (0.18 oz)

DIFFICULTY	
PREP TIME	30 MIN
REST TIME	1 HOUR

ADDITIVE Gg

TOOL

GELIFICATION : GELLAN FLAKES

DIRECTIONS

RASPBERRY FLAKES

1. Bring the vinegar and sugar to a boil. Using a spoon, dissolve the **GELLAN GUM** into the preparation and cook for 2 minutes. Refrigerate for 1 hour or until the preparation is completely congealed.

2. Unmold the congealed preparation and grate it onto a plate.

DRESSING

1. In a bowl, mix together the crumbled goat's cheese, raspery vinegar, olive oil, salt and pepper.

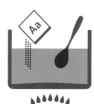

Add the **GELLAN GUM** to the preparation and cook for 2 minutes

Pour into a mold to refrigerate

SERVING SUGGESTION

Arrange the raspberry flakes, shoots and pecans on a plate. Drizzle the shoots with the dressing.

Unmold gel and grate

WINE VINEGAR STUFFED STRAWBERRIES

INGREDIENTS

Strawberries	4
Red wine vinegar	½ cup (120 ml)
Sugar	0.35 oz (10 g)

ADDITIVE

KAPPA CARRAGEENAN	2 g (0.07 oz)

DIFFICULTY

PREP TIME   10 MINUTES

REST TIME   20 MINUTES

ADDITIVE   Kc

TOOL

DIRECTIONS

1. Cut the white center out of each strawberry.
2. Bring the vinegar and the sugar to a boil. Add the **KAPPA CARRAGEENAN** and mix it with a hand blender while continuing to cook for 2 minutes.
3. Draw small quantities of the preparation into a pipette and use the pipette to fill the inside of the strawberries. Refrigerate for 20 minutes.

SERVING SUGGESTION

Sprinkle a generous layer of sugar across a plate and place the strawberries on it.

GELIFICATION : CARRAGEENAN GEL

Add the KAPPA CARRAGEENAN
to the warm preparation and
mix while heating

Fill a pipette with
the preparation

Fill the strawberries

SURPRISE CRANBERRY JELLY

INGREDIENTS

CRANBERRY JUICE GEL

Cranberry juice	1½ cups (350 ml)

LEMON JUICE PEARLS

Water	⅔ cup (160 ml)
Lemon Juice	¼ cup (60 ml)
Sugar	1.75 oz (50 g)
Cold vegetable oil	2 cups (470 ml)

TAPIOCA

Milk	1 cup (235 ml)
Sugar	0.5 oz (15 g)
Tapioca	0.7 oz (20 g)

ADDITIVE

AGAR-AGAR	3 g + 2 g (2½ sachet)

DIFFICULTY	♟♟	
PREP TIME	40 MIN	
REST TIME	1 HOUR	
ADDITIVE	Aa	
TOOL		
TIPS & TRICKS	P. 18	

DIRECTIONS

CRANBERRY JUICE GEL

1. Bring the cranberry juice and 3 g (1½ sachet) of the **AGAR-AGAR** to a boil and continue boiling for 2 minutes. Refrigerate for 1 hour.

2. Unmold the gel and cut it into small pieces. Mix in a blender until smooth.

LEMON JUICE PEARLS

1. Put the 2 cups of vegetable oil in the freezer for at least 30 minutes.

2. Bring the lemon juice, water, sugar and 2 g (1 sachet) of the **AGAR-AGAR** to a boil. Remove from stove and let sit uncovered for 5 minutes.

3. Pour the cold oil into a glass measuring no less than 6 inches (15 cm) in height.

4. Fill a pipette with the lemon juice preparation and drip it into the cold oil. Let sit for 2 minutes.

5. Using a sieve, scoop up the pearls from the oil and rinse them in warm water.

TAPIOCA

1. Bring the milk, sugar and tapioca to a boil. Let simmer for 5 minutes, stirring constantly.

2. Remove from stove, cover and let sit for 20 minutes.

3. Using a sieve, rinse the tapioca in water.

SERVING SUGGESTION

In a bowl, delicately stir together the cranberry juice gel, lemon juice pearls and tapioca pearls using a rubber spatula. Serve in small glasses.

GELIFICATION : AGAR-AGAR PEARLS

Add **AGAR-AGAR** to the preparation and bring to a boil

Drip into a tall glass of cold vegetable oil

Scoop up with a sieve and rinse with water

CHOCOLATE SPAGHETTI AND ORANGE JELLY

INGREDIENTS

CHOCOLATE SPAGHETTI

Milk	1 cup (235 ml)
Dark Chocolate	3 oz (85 g)
Tia Maria	2 tbsp (30 ml)
Ice cubes	20
Cold water	1 large bowl

ORANGE JELLY

Orange juice	½ cup (120 ml)

ADDITIVE

AGAR-AGAR	2 g + 1 g (1 ½ sachet)

DIFFICULTY	♟ ♟ ♟
PREP TIME	25 MIN
REST TIME	1 HOUR

ADDITIVE

TOOLS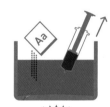

TIPS & TRICKS	P. 20

DIRECTIONS

CHOCOLATE SPAGHETTI

1. Bring the milk and 2 g (1 sachet) of the **AGAR-AGAR** to a boil.

2. Add the chocolate and mix it in well until it melts. Remove from the stove and mix in the Tia Maria until it is evenly distributed throughout.

3. Place the ice cubes in a large bowl, then fill with cold water.

4. Use the syringe to siphon off some of the chocolate and Tia Maria preparation and inject it into the silicone tubes.

5. Immerse the silicone tubes in cold water for 4 minutes.

6. Use the syringe to inject air into the silicone tubes and eject the spaghetti.

ORANGE JELLY

1. Bring the orange juice and 1 g (½ sachet) of the **AGAR-AGAR** to a boil and continue boiling for 2 minutes while stirring. Refrigerate for 1 hour or until the preparation is completely congealed.

2. Unmold the gel and cut it into small pieces. Mix in a blender until smooth. Fill a pipette with this mixture.

SERVING SUGGESTION

Serve the chocolate and Tia Maria spaghetti on a plate and garnish it with drops of orange jelly using the pipette.

GELIFICATION: AGAR-AGAR SPAGHETTIS

Add AGAR-AGAR to the preparation and bring to a boil

Using a syringe, fill a silicone tube with the preparation

Cool down

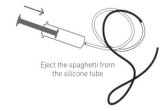

Eject the spaghetti from the silicone tube

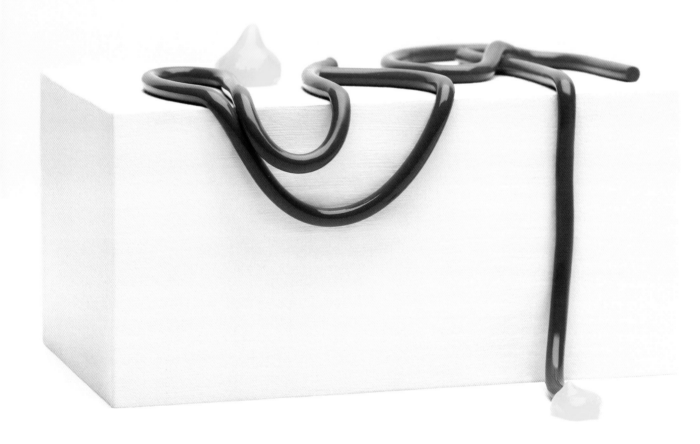

DIFFICULTY	♟ ♟ ♟
PREP TIME	15 MIN
REST TIME	15 MIN

ADDITIVES

TOOL

TIPS & TRICKS   P. 22

INGREDIENTS

Honey	¼ cup (60 ml)
Water	¾ cup (180 ml)
Apricot jelly	½ cup (120 ml)

ADDITIVES

AGAR-AGAR	2 g (1 sachet)
POPPING SUGAR	1 oz (30 g)

DIRECTIONS

1. Bring the honey, water and **AGAR-AGAR** to a boil.

2. Remove from stove and let sit, uncovered, for 5 minutes.

3. Pour a thin layer of the mixture onto a rectangular plate or a small baking sheet and let sit for 10 minutes.

4. Using a knife or cookie cutter, cut the gelified sheet into rectangular pieces.

SERVING SUGGESTION

Place a small amount of apricot jelly, sprinkled with a pinch of **POPPING SUGAR**, in the middle of each rectangle. Fold the gelified sheet to create a ravioli.

GELIFICATION : AGAR-AGAR SHEETS

Add **AGAR-AGAR** to the
preparation and bring
to a boil

Pour in flat plate to freeze

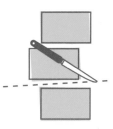

Cut the gel into
rectangular pieces

Fill and fold to
form a ravioli

TOMATO BALSAMIC CANNELLONI

INGREDIENTS

TOMATO CANNELLONI

Canned tomato juice	1 cup (235 ml)

GOAT'S CHEESE FILLING

Soft goat's cheese	3.5 oz (100 g)
Fresh thyme, chopped	0.5 oz (15 g)
Chives, chopped	0.5 oz (15 g)
Pepper	to taste

BALSAMIC VINEGAR PEARLS

Balsamic vinegar	¾ cup (180 ml)
Cold vegetable oil	2 cups (470 ml)

ADDITIVE

AGAR-AGAR	2 x 2 g (2 sachets)

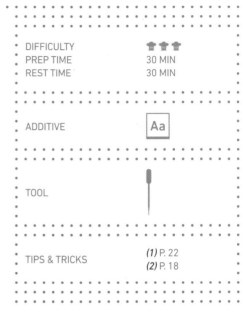

DIFFICULTY	♟ ♟ ♟
PREP TIME	30 MIN
REST TIME	30 MIN
ADDITIVE	Aa
TOOL	
TIPS & TRICKS	*(1)* P. 22
	(2) P. 18

DIRECTIONS

TOMATO CANNELLONI *(1)*

1. Bring the tomato juice and 2 g (1 sachet) of **AGAR-AGAR** to a boil while stirring. Remove from stove and let sit for 5 minutes.

2. Pour the mixture onto a rectangular plate or onto a small baking tray and place it in the fridge for 10 minutes. Using a knife, cut the sheet of tomato juice into rectangular pieces.

GOAT'S CHEESE FILLING

1. Mix all the ingredients together using a spatula. Transfer the goat's cheese mixture into a pastry bag and reserve.

BALSAMIC VINEGAR PEARLS *(2)*

1. Put the 2 cups of vegetable oil in the freezer for at least 30 minutes.

2. Bring the balsamic vinegar and 2 g (1 sachet) of **AGAR-AGAR** to a boil. Remove from the stove and let sit uncovered for 5 minutes.

3. Pour the cold oil into a glass measuring no less than 6 inches (15 cm) in height.

4. Fill a pipette with the balsamic vinegar preparation and drip it into the cold oil. Let sit for 2 minutes.

5. Using a sieve, remove the pearls from the oil and rinse them in warm water.

SERVING SUGGESTION

Place a small amount of goat's cheese filling in the middle of each rectangle. Fold the gelified sheet to create a ravioli. Serve alongside the balsamic vinegar pearls.

GELIFICATION : AGAR-AGAR CANNELONNI *(1)*

Add AGAR-AGAR to the preparation and bring to a boil

Pour onto flat rectangular plate to refrigerate

Cut the gel into rectangular pieces

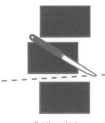

Fill and fold to form a ravioli

DESTRUCTURED RASPBERRIES

INGREDIENTS

RASPBERRY SYRUP

Water	2 cups (470 ml)
Sugar	¼ cup (60 ml)
Raspberries	1 cup (235 ml)

VANILLA POWDER

Vegetable oil	1 cup (235 ml)
Vanilla	1 pod

ADDITIVES

COLD SOLUBLE GELATIN	8 g (2 sachets)
AGAR-AGAR	2 g (1 sachet)
TAPIOCA MALTODEXTRIN	100 g (3.5 oz)

DIFFICULTY	♔ ♔ ♔ ♔ ♔
PREP TIME	40 MIN
REST TIME	3 HOURS

ADDITIVES   G   Aa   M

TOOL

DIRECTIONS

RASPBERRY SYRUP

1. Bring all ingredients to a boil and cook for 30 minutes.
2. Refrigerate for 30 minutes, then strain through a sieve to obtain a raspberry syrup. Reserve to make the raspberry sponge and raspberry gel.

RASPBERRY SPONGE

1. Measure 1¼ cups (300 ml) of the raspberry syrup. In a cylindrical container, use a hand blender to incorporate the **COLD SOLUBLE GELATIN** into the syrup. Let sit for 5 minutes.
2. Pour the mixture into a large oval-bottom bowl. Whip the mixture with a whisk for 10 minutes, as you would for a meringue.
3. Pour the preparation into a flat-bottom container with sides measuring between ¾ and 1½ inches (about 3 cm) in height. Refrigerate for 3 hours.

RASPBERRY GEL

1. Measure ⅔ cup (160 ml) of the raspberry syrup. Add the **AGAR-AGAR** and bring to a boil. Continue boiling for 2 minutes while stirring.
2. Refrigerate for 1 hour or until the preparation is completely congealed.
3. Unmold the gel and cut it into small pieces. Mix in a blender until smooth. Fill a pipette with this mixture.

VANILLA POWDER

1. Cook the vanilla with the oil on low heat for 20 minutes. Let sit for 3 hours.
2. Using a fork, gradually mix the **TAPIOCA MALTODEXTRIN** with 1 tbsp (15 ml) of the vanilla oil until a powder is obtained.

SERVING SUGGESTION

Carve out portions of the sponge using a knife. If not prepared immediately before serving, refrigerate. Serve the raspberry sponge on a plate and garnish it with drops of raspberry gel using the pipette. Sprinkle with vanilla powder.

GELIFICATION: GELATIN SPONGE

Add the **COLD SOLUBLE GELATIN** to the preparation

Mix well using a hand blender

In a bowl, whip with a whisk to form a meringue, then pour into a mold to refrigerate

INGREDIENTS

TOMATO SPONGE

Tomatoes	4 or 5
Salt	to taste
Pepper	to taste

BALSAMIC VINEGAR PEARLS

Balsamic vinegar	¾ cup (180 ml)
Cold vegetable oil	2 cups (470 ml)

BASIL POWDER

Basil leaves	1.75 oz (50 g)
Vegetable oil	¾ cup (180 ml)

ADDITIVES

COLD SOLUBLE GELATIN	4 g (1 sachet)
AGAR-AGAR	2 g (1 sachet)
TAPIOCA MALTODEXTRIN	100 g (3.5 oz)

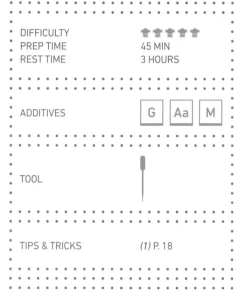

DIFFICULTY	🐔🐔🐔🐔🐔
PREP TIME	45 MIN
REST TIME	3 HOURS

ADDITIVES　　G　Aa　M

TOOL

TIPS & TRICKS　　(1) P. 18

DIRECTIONS

TOMATO SPONGE

1. Peel the tomatoes. Use a blender to liquefy the tomatoes into a coulis. Strain the coulis through a sieve and reserve ¾ cup (180 ml) of tomato juice without pulp.

2. In a cylindrical container, use a hand blender to incorporate the **COLD SOLUBLE GELATIN** into the tomato juice. Let sit for 5 minutes.

3. Pour the mixture into a large oval-bottom bowl. Whip the mixture with a whisk for 10 minutes, as you would for a meringue.

4. Pour the preparation into a flat-bottom container with sides measuring between ¾ and 1½ inches (about 3 cm) in height. Refrigerate for 3 hours.

BALSAMIC VINEGAR PEARLS [1]

1. Put the 2 cups of vegetable oil in the freezer for at least 30 minutes.

2. Bring the balsamic vinegar and the **AGAR-AGAR** to a boil. Remove from the stove and let sit, uncovered, for 5 minutes.

3. Pour the cold oil into a glass measuring no less than 6 inches (15 cm) in height.

4. Fill a pipette with the balsamic vinegar preparation and drip it into the cold oil. Let sit for 2 minutes.

5. Using a sieve, remove the pearls from the oil and rinse them in warm water.

BASIL POWDER

1. Use a blender to mix the basil and the vegetable oil. Let sit for 3 hours.

2. Filter the mixture carefully through a sieve and reserve 1 tbsp (15 ml) of green oil.

3. Using a fork, gradually mix the **TAPIOCA MALTODEXTRIN** with the green oil until a powder is obtained.

SERVING SUGGESTION

Carve out portions of the sponge using a round cookie cutter. If not prepared immediately before serving, refrigerate. Arrange on a plate next to the balsamic vinegar pearls and basil powder.

GELIFICATION : GELATIN SPONGE

Add the COLD SOLUBLE GELATIN to the preparation

Mix well using a hand blender

In a bowl, whip with a whisk to form a meringue, then pour into a mold to refrigerate

TRANSFORMED MUSHROOM PENNE

INGREDIENTS

WHIPPED MUSHROOM CREAM

35% cooking cream	1 cup (235 ml)
Dehydrated mushrooms	0.35 oz (10 g)
Salt	to taste
Pepper	to taste

CHICKEN BROTH PENNE

Chicken broth	1⅓ cups (320 ml)
Soy sauce	3 tbsp (45 ml)
Ice cubes	20
Cold water	1 large bowl

SAUTEED MUSHROOMS

Wild mushrooms	3.5 oz (100 g)
Butter	1 tsp (5 ml)
Salt	to taste
Pepper	to taste

ADDITIVE

AGAR-AGAR	4 g (2 sachets)

DIFFICULTY	♣ ♣ ♣ ♣
PREP TIME	50 MIN
REST TIME	2 HOURS

ADDITIVE	Aa

TOOL	

DIRECTIONS

WHIPPED MUSHROOM CREAM

1. Let the dried mushrooms, the cream and the salt and pepper simmer on low heat for 15 minutes. Remove from stove, cover with a lid, and let sit for 45 minutes covered with a lid.

2. Strain the contents through a sieve into a bowl and refrigerate for at least 1 hour.

3. Whisk the contents until a whipped cream consistency is reached, then transfer it to a pastry bag fitted with a very small tip. Set aside.

CHICKEN BROTH PENNE

1. Bring the chicken broth, soy sauce and the **AGAR-AGAR** to a boil and continue boiling for 2 minutes while stirring. Remove from stove and let sit, uncovered, for 10 minutes.

2. Place the ice cubes in a large bowl, then fill with cold water. Place a metal rod into the water for 10 seconds.

3. Take the now-cold metal rod and place it in the broth for 4 seconds, then remove it and let it sit for 30 seconds.

4. Delicately remove the now-gelified broth cylinder from the metal rod and place it on a plate. Refrigerate for 20 minutes.

5. Repeat steps 3 and 4 until enough gel cylinders are made. Refrigerate 10 minutes.

SAUTEED MUSHROOMS

1. Sauté the mushrooms with butter in a pan. Season with salt and pepper to taste.

SERVING SUGGESTION

Slice the tip of of the chicken-broth cylinder into penne-shaped pieces. Using the pastry bag and a small tip, stuff the penne with the whipped mushroom cream. Serve the sauteed mushrooms on the plate alternately with the penne.

GELIFICATION

Add **AGAR-AGAR** to the preparation and bring to a boil

Make a metal rod cold

Dip the cold metal rod into the agar-agar preparation

Delicately remove gelified cylinder from metal rod

SPHERIFICATION
Recipes

BELL PEPPER BUBBLES ON OLIVES

INGREDIENTS

BELL PEPPER SPHERES

Red bell pepper	1
Yellow bell pepper	1
Orange bell pepper	1
Water	2 cups (470 ml)

OLIVE TAPENADE

Pitted green olives	10.6 oz (300 g)
Garlic, chopped	1 clove
Olive oil	1 tbsp (15 ml)

ADDITIVES

CALCIUM LACTATE	3 x 1g (⅗ sachet)
SODIUM ALGINATE	2g (1 sachet)

DIFFICULTY		
PREP TIME		35 MIN
REST TIME		1 HOUR
ADDITIVES		
TOOLS		
TIPS & TRICKS		P. 42

FROZEN REVERSE SPHERIFICATION

DIRECTIONS

BELL PEPPER SPHERES

1. Wash and trim bell peppers.
2. Using a hand blender, mix the red bell pepper until a puree is obtained. Add water if needed. Strain the mixture through a sieve and reserve 1 cup (235 ml) of the red bell pepper coulis.
3. Weigh 1g (⅕ sachet) of **CALCIUM LACTATE** and dissolve it onto the red bell pepper coulis using a spoon. Pour the mixture into half-spherical molds. Place in the freezer for 1 hour or until the spheres are completely frozen.
4. Repeat steps 2 and 3 with the yellow and orange bell peppers.
5. Using a hand blender, dissolve the **SODIUM ALGINATE** into the water and let sit for 5 minutes.
6. Remove the frozen bell pepper spheres from the mold and place them in the sodium alginate bath. Let sit for 5 minutes while stirring delicately with a spoon.
7. Using a slotted spoon, scoop out the spheres, rinse them in a bowl of water and remove excess moisture by blotting the bottom of the slotted spoon against a paper towel.

OLIVE TAPENADE

1. Mix all ingredients together in a blender until a puree is obtained.

Add **CALCIUM LACTATE** to the preparation and pour into half-spherical silicone molds to freeze

Submerge the frozen preparation into a **SODIUM ALGINATE** bath

SERVING SUGGESTION

Serve the tapenade in serving spoons and decorate each spoon with a bell pepper sphere.

Rinse and serve

BLOODY SPHERE

INGREDIENTS

Clamato juice	1¼ cups (300 ml)
Water	2 cups (470 ml)
Cucumber	1
Pepper	to taste
Lemon juice	a dash

ADDITIVES

CALCIUM LACTATE	1.6 g (⅓ sachet)
SODIUM ALGINATE	2 g (1 sachet)

DIFFICULTY ♟♟
PREP TIME 15 MIN
REST TIME 1 HOUR

ADDITIVES Cl Sa

TOOLS

TIPS & TRICKS P. 42

DIRECTIONS

1. Cut ¼ of the cucumber into a brunoise and add it to the the Clamato juice.

2. Using a spoon, dissolve the **CALCIUM LACTATE** into the Clamato juice preparation.

3. Pour the mixture into half-spherical molds and place in the freezer for 1 hour or until the spheres are completely frozen.

4. Using a hand blender, dissolve the **SODIUM ALGINATE** into the water and let sit for 5 minutes.

5. Remove the frozen Clamato spheres from the molds and place them in the sodium alginate bath. Let sit for 5 minutes while stirring delicately with a spoon.

6. Using a slotted spoon, scoop up the spheres, rinse them in a bowl of water and remove excess moisture by blotting the bottom of the slotted spoon against a paper towel.

SERVING SUGGESTION

Serve the Clamato juice spheres on a slice of cucumber with some freshly-gound pepper and a dash of lemon juice.

FROZEN RESERVE SPHERIFICATION

Add **CALCIUM LACTATE** to the preparation and pour into half-spherical silicone molds to freeze

Submerge the frozen preparation into a **SODIUM ALGINATE** bath

Rinse and serve

DIFFICULTY	♟♟	
PREP TIME	35 MIN	
REST TIME	30 MIN	

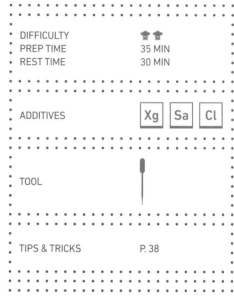

ADDITIVES — Xg Sa Cl

TOOL

TIPS & TRICKS — P. 38

INGREDIENTS

Black tea	1 tea bag
Orange tea	1 tea bag
Mint tea	1 tea bag
Hibiscus tea	1 tea bag
Water	4 cups (940 ml)
Sugar	2 oz (60 g)
Edible flowers	to taste

ADDITIVES

XANTHAN GUM	0.5 g (½ sachet)
SODIUM ALGINATE	3 x 1 g (1½ sachet)
CALCIUM LACTATE	2 g (⅖ sachet)

DIRECTIONS

1. Brew 1 cup (235 ml) of black tea with 0.5 oz (15 g) of the sugar. Mix in 0.5 oz (15 g) of the **XANTHAN GUM** by stirring it in with a spoon, then let cool.

2. Brew 1 cup (235 ml) of orange tea with 0.5 oz (15 g) of the sugar. Mix in 1 g (½ sachet) of **SODIUM ALGINATE** using a hand blender, then let cool.

3. Repeat step 2 with the mint tea and the hibiscus tea.

4. Dissolve the **CALCIUM LACTATE** in 2 cups (470 ml) of water.

5. Fill a pipette with the orange tea mixture and drip droplets into the calcium lactate bath. Let sit for 3 minutes.

6. Using a sieve, remove the pearls from the calcium lactate bath and rinse them in warm water.

7. Repeat steps 5 and 6 with the mint tea and the hibiscus tea mixtures.

SERVING SUGGESTION

Fill a test tube with black tea and add a few pearls of each of the other three teas. Decorate with a few edible flower petals.

BASIC SPHERIFICATION

Add **SODIUM ALGINATE** to the preparation

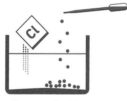

Drop preparation into **CALCIUM LACTATE** bath

Scoop up with a sieve and rinse with water

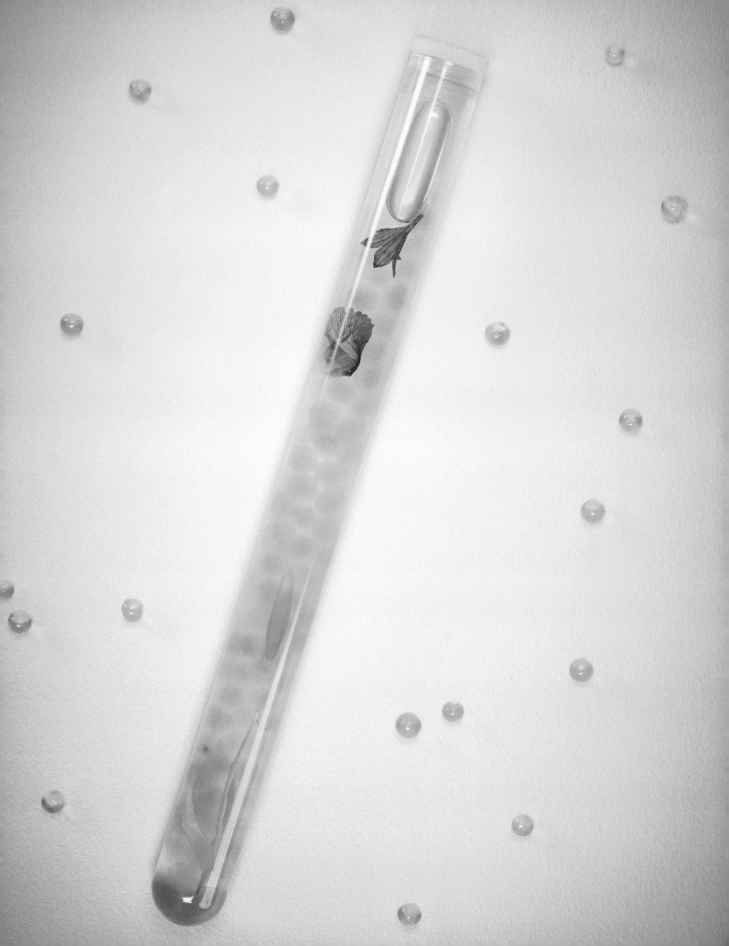

DECONSTRUCTED COCOA

INGREDIENTS

COCOA SPHERIFICATION

Water	3¼ cups (770 ml)
Sugar	1oz (30 g)
Cocoa powder	1oz (30 g)

WHITE CHOCOLATE CREAM

35% cooking cream	1¼ cups (300 ml)
White chocolate, chopped	3.5 oz (100 g)

ADDITIVES

SODIUM ALGINATE	1g (½ sachet)
CALCIUM LACTATE	3 g (⅗ sachet)

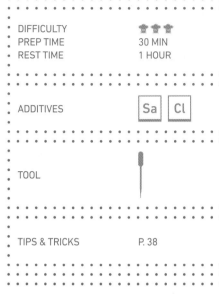

DIFFICULTY	👨‍🍳 👨‍🍳 👨‍🍳
PREP TIME	30 MIN
REST TIME	1 HOUR
ADDITIVES	Sa Cl
TOOL	
TIPS & TRICKS	P. 38

DIRECTIONS

COCOA SPHERIFICATION

1. Bring the sugar, cocoa powder and 1¼ cups (300 ml) of the water to a boil and continue cooking for 2 minutes. Using a hand blender, incorporate the **SODIUM ALGINATE** into the preparation and let sit for 1 hour.

2. Using a spoon, dissolve the **CALCIUM LACTATE** into 2 cups (470 ml) of the water. Fill a pipette with the chocolate preparation and drip it into the calcium lactate bath. Let sit for 3 minutes.

3. Using a sieve, remove the pearls from the calcium lactate bath and rinse them in warm water.

WHITE CHOCOLATE CREAM

1. Bring the cream to a boil and pour it into a bowl with the white chocolate; stir, then set aside until cool.

SERVING SUGGESTION:

Pour the white chocolate cream into serving spoons, distribute some cocoa pearls on top and serve.

BASIC SPHERIFICATION

Add **SODIUM ALGINATE** to the preparation

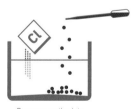

Drop preparation into **CALCIUM LACTATE** bath

Scoop up with a sieve and rinse with water

ENCAPSULATED PIÑA COLADA

INGREDIENTS

ENCAPSULATED PIÑA COLADA

White rum	¼ cup (60 ml)
Brown rum	¼ cup (60 ml)
Sweetened coconut milk	½ cup (120 ml)
Pineapple juice	1 cup (235 ml)
Water	2 cups (470 ml)

CHERRY FOAM

Maraschino cherry syrup	1⅓ cups (320 ml)
Pineapple, diced	½ cup (120 ml)

ADDITIVES

CALCIUM LACTATE	1.6 g (⅓ sachet)
SODIUM ALGINATE	2 g (1 sachet)
SOY LECITHIN	2 g (1 sachet)

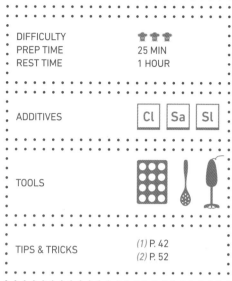

DIFFICULTY	♟♟♟
PREP TIME	25 MIN
REST TIME	1 HOUR
ADDITIVES	Cl Sa Sl
TOOLS	
TIPS & TRICKS	(1) P. 42 (2) P. 52

FROZEN REVERSE SPHERIFICATION[1]

DIRECTIONS

ENCAPSULATED PIÑA COLADA[1]

1. Pour the white rum, the dark rum, the sweetened coconut milk and the pineapple juice into a bowl. Using a spoon, mix in the **CALCIUM LACTATE**.
2. Pour the mixture into half spherical molds and place in the freezer for 1 hour or until the spheres are completely frozen.
3. Using a hand blender, dissolve the **SODIUM ALGINATE** into the water and let sit for 5 minutes.
4. Remove the frozen piña colada spheres from the mold and place them in the sodium alginate bath. Let sit for 5 minutes. while stirring delicately with a spoon.
5. Using a slotted spoon, scoop out the spheres, rinse them in a bowl of water and remove excess moisture by blotting the bottom of the slotted spoon against a paper towel.

CHERRY FOAM[2]

1. Combine maraschino cherry syrup and the **SOY LECITHIN** in a flat-bottomed rectangular bowl.
2. Using a hand blender, incorporate air bubles into the solution for 3 to 4 minutes and let sit for 5 minutes. Scoop off the foam with a spoon.

SERVING SUGGESTION

Serve the piña colada spheres on top of the diced pineapple, garnished with cherry foam.

Add **CALCIUM LACTATE** to the preparation and pour into half-spherical silicone molds to freeze

Submerge the frozen preparation into a **SODIUM ALGINATE** bath

Rinse and serve

HAM-WRAPPED MELON SUSHI

INGREDIENTS

Cantaloupe melon	1
Sugar	0.5 oz (15 g)
Water	2 cups (470 ml)
Prosciutto	6 slices
Olive oil	2 tbsp (30 ml)
Orange zest	to taste
Pepper	to taste
Olive oil	to taste

ADDITIVES

SODIUM ALGINATE	1 g (½ sachet)
CALCIUM LACTATE	2 g (⅔ sachet)

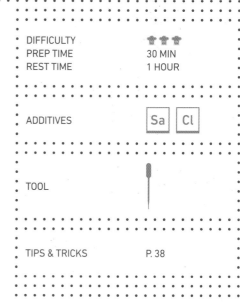

DIFFICULTY	♟ ♟ ♟
PREP TIME	30 MIN
REST TIME	1 HOUR
ADDITIVES	Sa Cl
TOOL	
TIPS & TRICKS	P. 38

DIRECTIONS

1. Peel the melon and cut it into cubes.

2. Process the cubes of cantaloupe in a blender until a uniform texture is obtained and strain the contents through a sieve.

3. Take 1 cup (235 ml) of the cantaloupe coulis made in the previous step and mix in the sugar and **SODIUM ALGINATE** using a hand blender. Let the coulis sit for 1 hour.

4. Dissolve the **CALCIUM LACTATE** in the water by stirring it in with a spoon. Fill a pipette with some cantaloupe coulis and drip droplets of it into the calcium lactate bath. Let sit for 3 minutes.

5. Using a sieve, remove the pearls from the calcium lactate bath and rinse them in warm water.

SERVING SUGGESTION

Wrap a slice of prosciutto around a crouton of bread to create a bowl shape. Fill this bowl with the melon caviar, garnish with the zest and pepper and drizzle with olive oil.

BASIC SPHERIFICATION

Add **SODIUM ALGINATE** to the preparation

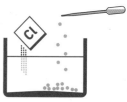

Drop preparation into **CALCIUM LACTATE** bath

Scoop up with a sieve and rinse with water

INGREDIENTS

Yellow habanero peppers	15
Red habanero peppers	15
Jalapeño peppers	15
Water	3 cups (720 ml)
Avocado	1
Lemon	1
Cilantro	to taste

ADDITIVES

SODIUM ALGINATE	3 x 1g (1 ½ sachet)
CALCIUM LACTATE	2 g (⅔ sachet)

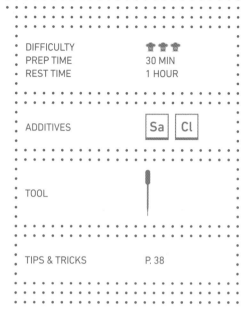

DIFFICULTY	👨‍🍳👨‍🍳👨‍🍳
PREP TIME	30 MIN
REST TIME	1 HOUR

ADDITIVES	Sa	Cl

TOOL

TIPS & TRICKS   P. 38

DIRECTIONS

1. Cut peppers and remove seeds.

2. Using a hand blender, incorporate the yellow habanero peppers into ⅔ cup (160 ml) of the water. Strain the mixture through a sieve and reserve 1 cup (235 ml) of the pepper coulis. Using a hand blender, incorporate 1g (½ sachet) of the **SODIUM ALGINATE** into the coulis and let sit for 1 hour.

3. Repeat step 2 with the red habanero peppers and the jalapeño peppers

4. Using a spoon, dissolve the **CALCIUM LACTATE** in 2 cups (470 ml) of water.

5. Fill a pipette with the yellow habanero pepper coulis mixture and drip it into the calcium lactate bath. Let sit for 3 minutes. Using a sieve, remove the pearls from the bath and rinse them in warm water.

6. Repeat step 5 with the red habanero pepper coulis and the jalapeño pepper coulis.

7. Peel the avocado and cut it into thin rectangular slices.

8. Press the lemon and dip the avocado slices into its juice.

SERVING SUGGESTION

Arrange the pepper coulis pearls and avocado slices on a plate and garnish with cilantro.

BASIC SPHERIFICATION

Add **SODIUM ALGINATE** to the preparation

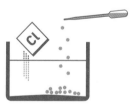

Drop preparation into **CALCIUM LACTATE** bath

Scoop up with a sieve and rinse with water

RECONSTRUCTED OLIVES

INGREDIENTS

OLIVE SPHERES

Pitted green olives	18 oz (500 g)
Water	2 cups (470 ml)

MARINADE

Olive oil	1 cup (235 ml)
Garlic	2 cloves
Bell peppers	4
Bay leaf	1
Rosemary sprigs	2
Thyme sprigs	2

ADDITIVES

CALCIUM LACTATE	1 g (⅛ sachet)
SODIUM ALGINATE	2 g (1 sachet)

DIFFICULTY	
PREP TIME	20 MIN
REST TIME	1 HOUR
ADDITIVES	Cl Sa
TOOLS	
TIPS & TRICKS	P. 42

FROZEN REVERSE SPHERIFICATION

DIRECTIONS

OLIVE SPHERES

1. Place the olives in a blender for 3 minutes to form a very thin puree.

2. Place the puree in a cheesecloth and squeeze it until roughly 1 cup (235 ml) of olive juice is obtained.

3. Using a spoon, dissolve the **CALCIUM LACTATE** in the olive juice and pour the mixture into half-spherical molds. Place in the freezer for 1 hour or until the spheres are completely frozen.

4. Using a hand blender, dissolve the **SODIUM ALGINATE** into the water and let sit for 5 minutes.

5. Remove the frozen olive juice spheres from the mold and place them in the sodium alginate bath. Let sit for 5 minutes while stirring delicately with a spoon.

6. Using a slotted spoon, scoop out the spheres, rinse them in a bowl of water and remove excess moisture by blotting the bottom of the slotted spoon against a paper towel.

MARINADE

1. Chop the bell peppers into small pieces.

2. Heat the olive oil in a frying pan and roast the garlic.

3. Add all the other ingredients and cook for 2 minutes, then remove from the stove and let cool to room temperature.

SERVING SUGGESTION

Distribute a thin layer of marinade across a plate and serve the spheres on it.

Add **CALCIUM LACTATE** to the preparation and pour into half-spherical silicone molds to freeze

Submerge the frozen preparation into a **SODIUM ALGINATE** bath

Rinse and serve

BUBBLE-GUM FONDANT

INGREDIENTS

3.25% milk	1 cup (235 ml)
Sugar	0.5 oz (15 g)
Bubble gum	3 pieces
Red food coloring	3 drops
Water	2 cups (470 ml)
Candy floss	1.75 oz (50 g)

ADDITIVES

CALCIUM LACTATE	1 g (⅛ sachet)
COLD SOLUBLE GELATIN	6 g (1½ sachet)
SODIUM ALGINATE	2 g (1 sachet)

DIFFICULTY	♟ ♟ ♟ ♟
PREP TIME	30 MIN
REST TIME	2 HOURS 15 MIN

ADDITIVES Cl G Sa

TOOL

TIPS & TRICKS P. 40

DIRECTIONS

1. In a pan, simmer the milk, sugar and gum for 15 minutes. Remove from stove and let sit for 1 hour. Strain the mixture through a sieve.

2. Using a spoon, dissolve the **CALCIUM LACTATE** and **COLD SOLUBLE GELATINE** in the bubble gum preparation. Pour in a plastic container to form a layer about ¾ inch (2 cm) thick and place in the freezer for 3 hours or until the preparation is completely congealed.

3. Using a hand blender, dissolve the **SODIUM ALGINATE** in the water and let sit for 5 minutes.

4. Remove the congealed preparation from the plastic container and cut it into cubes. Place the cubes in the alginate bath and let sit for 5 minutes while delicately stirring with a spoon.

5. Using a slotted spoon, collect the cubes, rinse them in a bowl of water and remove excess moisture by blotting the bottom of the slotted spoon against a paper towel.

SERVING SUGGESTION

Heat the fondants for 5 seconds in the microwave oven and serve on top of the candy floss.

REVERSE SPHERIFICATION

Add **CALCIUM LACTATE** and **COLD SOLUBLE GELATIN** to the preparation and pour in a container to freeze

Cut the frozen preparation into cubes and submerge into a **SODIUM ALGINATE** bath

Rinse and serve

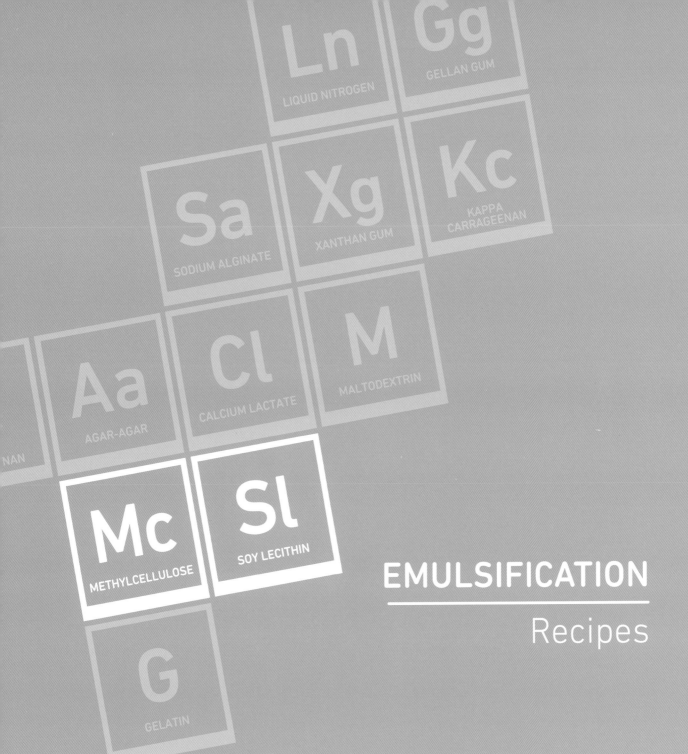

EMULSIFICATION

Recipes

CLOUD OF CHIPS

INGREDIENTS

Malt vinegar	¾ cup (180 ml)
Water	¼ cup (60 ml)
Potato chips	1 bag

ADDITIVE

SOY LECITHIN	2 g (1 sachet)

DIFFICULTY		
PREP TIME		5 MIN
REST TIME		1 HOUR
ADDITIVE		SL
TOOL		
TIPS & TRICKS		P. 52

DIRECTIONS

1. Combine the vinegar, water and the **SOY LECITHIN** in a flat-bottomed rectangular bowl.
2. Using a hand blender, incorporate air bubbles into the solution for 3 to 4 minutes.
3. Scoop off the foam with a spoon and place it into another container.
4. If necessary, repeat steps 2 and 3 to create and scoop off more foam.
5. Place in the freezer for 5 hours or until the foam is completely frozen.

SERVING SUGGESTION

Serve the malt vinegar foam with the chips.

SOY LECITHIN FOAM

Add the **SOY LECITHIN** to
the liquid preparation

Incorporate air bubbles
into the solution

Scoop off the foam and serve

REINVENTED CARPACCIO

INGREDIENTS

Prepared horseradish	¼ cup (60 ml)
Water	1 cup (235 ml)
Beef carpaccio, sliced	3.5 oz (100 g)

ADDITIVE

| SOY LECITHIN | 2 g (1 sachet) |

DIFFICULTY	
PREP TIME	5 MIN
REST TIME	5 MIN
ADDITIVE	Sl
TOOL	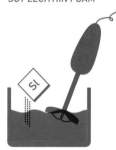
TIPS & TRICKS	P. 52

DIRECTIONS

1. Combine the prepared horseradish, water and the **SOY LECITHIN** in a flat-bottomed rectangular bowl.
2. Using a hand blender, incorporate air bubbles into the solution for 3 to 4 minutes and let sit for 5 minutes.
3. Scoop off the foam with a spoon.

SERVING SUGGESTION

Serve the carpaccio slices in serving spoons and decorate with a spoonful of horseradish foam.

SOY LECITHIN FOAM

Add the **SOY LECITHIN** to the liquid preparation

Incorporate air bubbles into the solution

Scoop off the foam and serve

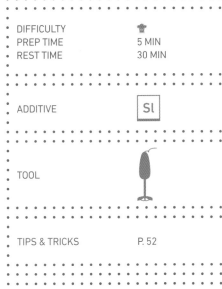

DIFFICULTY	
PREP TIME	5 MIN
REST TIME	30 MIN

| ADDITIVE | Sl |

| TOOL | |

| TIPS & TRICKS | P. 52 |

INGREDIENTS

HARISSA FOAM

Harissa	¼ cup (60 ml)
Water	¾ cup (180 ml)
Salt	1 tsp (5 ml)

GUACAMOLE

Avocado	1
Garlic, chopped	½ clove
Vegetable oil	2 tbsp (30 ml)
Salt	to taste
Pepper	to taste
Cilantro, chopped	to taste
Sour cream	2 tbsp (30 ml)
Tacos (hard shell)	1 box

ADDITIVE

| SOY LECITHIN | 2 g (1 sachet) |

DIRECTIONS

HARISSA FOAM

1. Combine all the ingredients and the **SOY LECITHIN** in a flat-bottomed rectangular bowl.
2. Using a hand blender, incorporate air bubbles into the solution for 3 to 4 minutes and let sit for 5 minutes.
3. Scoop off the foam with a spoon.

GUACAMOLE

1. Crush the avocado, garlic, oil, salt and pepper together.
2. Add the cilantro and mix well.

SERVING SUGGESTION

Fill a taco with the guacamole and sour cream and garnish with the harissa foam.

SOY LECITHIN FOAM

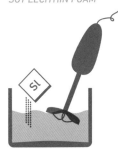

Add the **SOY LECITHIN** to the liquid preparation

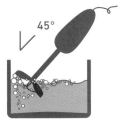

Incorporate air bubbles into the solution

Scoop off the foam and serve

INGREDIENTS

SOY SAUCE FOAM

Soy sauce	⅔ cup (160 ml)
Water	⅓ cup (80 ml)

LEMON FOAM

Lemon juice	¾ cup (180 ml)
Water	¼ cup (60 ml)

GINGER FOAM

Marinated ginger brine	½ cup (120 ml)
Water	⅓ cup (80 ml)

SALMON TARTARE

Salmon, chopped	7 oz (200 g)
Green onion, chopped	½
Garlic, chopped	½ clove
Chives, chopped	1 tbsp (15 ml)
Vegetable oil	2 tbsp (30 ml)
Salt	to taste
Pepper	to taste
Wasabi paste	1 oz (30 g)

ADDITIVE

SOY LECITHIN	3 x 2 g (3 sachets)

DIFFICULTY	🎩🎩
PREP TIME	20 MIN
REST TIME	5 MIN
ADDITIVE	Sl
TOOL	
TIPS & TRICKS	P. 52

DIRECTIONS

SOY SAUCE FOAM

1. Combine the soy sauce, water and 2 g (1 sachet) of the **SOY LECITHIN** in a flat-bottomed rectangular bowl.

2. Using a hand blender, incorporate air bubbles into the solution for 3 to 4 minutes and let sit for 5 minutes.

3. Scoop off the foam with a spoon.

LEMON FOAM

1. Combine the lemon juice, water and 2 g (1 sachet) of the **SOY LECITHIN** in a flat-bottomed rectangular bowl.

2. Using a hand blender, incorporate air bubbles into the solution for 3 to 4 minutes and let sit for 5 minutes.

3. Scoop off the foam with a spoon.

GINGER FOAM

1. Combine the brine, water and 2 g (1 sachet) of the **SOY LECITHIN** in a flat-bottomed rectangular bowl.

2. Using a hand blender, incorporate air bubbles into the solution for 3 to 4 minutes and let sit for 5 minutes.

3. Scoop off the foam with a spoon.

SALMON TARTARE

1. Mix all ingredients together. If prepared in advance, store in a closed container in the fridge.

SERVING SUGGESTION

Serve the tartare along with the three foams and decorate with pea-sized wasabi spheres created by rolling the paste between the palms of your hands.

SOY LECITHIN FOAM

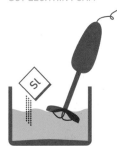

Add the **SOY LECITHIN** to the liquid preparation

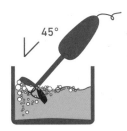

Incorporate air bubbles into the solution

Scoop off the foam and serve

INGREDIENTS

SUSPENDED RED BULL

Red Bull	1 cup (235 ml)
Pineapple, cut into a brunoise	1 tbsp (15 ml)

VANILLA FOAM

Water	1 cup (235 ml)
Sugar	0.5 oz (15 g)
Vanilla extract	6 drops

ADDITIVES

XANTHAN GUM	0.5 g (½ sachet)
SOY LECITHIN	2 g (1 sachet)

DIFFICULTY	🍄 🍄 🍄
PREP TIME	15 MIN
REST TIME	30 MIN

ADDITIVES	Xg	Ls

TOOL

TIPS & TRICKS	P. 52

DIRECTIONS

SUSPENDED RED BULL

1. Measure ½ cup (120 ml) of the Red Bull. Using a hand blender, incorporate the **XANTHAN GUM**. Let sit for 30 minutes.
2. Stir in the pineapple and remaining Red Bull delicately, just before serving.

VANILLA FOAM

1. Combine all the ingredients and the **SOY LECITHIN** in a flat-bottom rectangular bowl.
2. Using a hand blender, incorporate air bubles into the solution for 3 to 4 minutes and let sit for 5 minutes.
3. Scoop off the foam with a spoon.

SERVING SUGGESTION

Serve the Red Bull mixture in a clear glass and top it off with the vanilla foam.

SOY LECITHIN FOAM

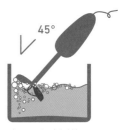

Add the **SOY LECITHIN** to the liquid preparation

45°

Incorporate air bubbles into the solution

Scoop off the foam and serve

BEET MERINGUE CANAPÉ

INGREDIENTS

BEET MERINGUE

Canned beet	1
Beet brine	¾ cup (180 ml)

ORANGE JELLY

Orange juice	¾ cup (180 ml)
Green apples, sliced	1.05 oz (30 g)
Feta cheese	1.05 oz (30 g)

ADDITIVES

METHYLCELLULOSE	2 g (0.07 oz)
XANTHAN GUM	0.5 g (½ sachet)
AGAR-AGAR	2 g (1 sachet)

DIFFICULTY	
PREP TIME	20 MIN
REST TIME	10 MIN
ADDITIVES	Mc Gx Aa
TOOL	
TIPS & TRICKS	(1) P. 22

DIRECTIONS

BEET MERINGUE

1. In a cylindrical container, use a hand blender to incorporate the canned beets, **METHYLCELLULOSE** and **XANTHAN GUM** into the beet brine.
2. Pour the preparation into the bowl of a mixer. Using the mixer's whisk attachment, whip the mixture for 10 minutes as you would for a meringue.

ORANGE JELLY[1]

1. In a saucepan, bring the orange juice and **AGAR-AGAR** to a boil and continue boiling for 2 minutes. Remove from the stove and let sit for 5 minutes.
2. Pour the mixture onto a rectangular plate or a small baking sheet and refrigerate for 10 minutes.
3. Using a knife, cut the sheet of gelified orange juice into rectangular pieces.

SERVING SUGGESTION

Garnish a slice of orange jelly with feta and apple slices and top it off with the beet meringue.

METHYLCELLULOSE MERINGUE

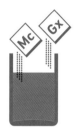

Add the MÉTHYLCELLULOSE and
XANTHAN GUM to the preparation

Mix well using
a hand blender

Whip for 10 minutes using
a mixer's whisk attachment

INGREDIENTS

Passion fruit juice	1¼ cups (300 ml)
Fresh passion fruits	3

ADDITIVES

METHYLCELLULOSE	4 g (0.15 oz)
COLD SOLUBLE GELATIN	8 g (2 sachets)

DIFFICULTY	🍄🍄🍄🍄
PREP TIME	30 MIN
REST TIME	1 HOUR

ADDITIVES   Mc G

TOOL

DIRECTIONS

1. In a cylindrical container, use a hand blender to incorporate the **METHYLCELLULOSE** into half of the passion fruit juice. Refrigerate for 1 hour or until the preparation has cooled down to 37.4°F (3°C).

2. Using a hand blender, incorporate the **COLD SOLUBLE GELATIN** into the rest of the passion fruit juice. Let sit for 10 minutes.

3. Preheat the oven to 176°F (80°C).

4. Let the refrigerated juice preparation sit on the counter for 30 minutes or until it warms up to a 57.2°F (14°C).

5. Pour the preparation into the bowl of a mixer. Using the mixer's whisk attachment, start whipping the mixture. As the foam starts forming, progressively start adding the mix of juice and cold soluble gelatin. Continue whipping for 10 minutes.

6. Pour the preparation onto a parchment-paper-lined baking sheet. Spread a 1 inch (3 cm) thin layer of the preparation using a spatula. Let dry in the oven for at least 1 hour.

SERVING SUGGESTION

Once dried, cut into cubes and serve with a spoonful of fresh passion fruit.

METHYLCELLULOSE MERINGUE

Add the **METHYLCELLULOSE** to one half of the preparation and the **COLD SOLUBLE GELATIN** to the other half.

Refrigerate the **METHYLCELLULOSE** mixture then, let it come back to room temperature

Let the **COLD SOLUBLE GELATIN** mixture sit for10 minutes

Whip the **METHYLCELLULOSE** mixture

Gradually add the **COLD SOLUBLE GELATIN** mixture to the **METHYLCELLULOSE** one while whipping

INGREDIENTS

| Peach juice | 1¼ cups (300 ml) |

ADDITIVES

| METHYLCELLULOSE | 4 g (0.15 oz) |
| COLD SOLUBLE GELATIN | 8 g (2 sachets) |

DIFFICULTY	♔ ♔ ♔ ♔
PREP TIME	30 MIN
REST TIME	1 HOUR 30 MIN

| ADDITIVES | Mc   G |

TOOL

DIRECTIONS

1. In a cylindrical container, use a hand blender to incorporate the **METHYLCELLULOSE** into half of the peach juice. Refrigerate for 1 hour or until the preparation has cooled down to 37.4°F (3°C).

2. Using a hand blender, incorporate the **COLD SOLUBLE GELATIN** into the rest of the peach juice. Let sit for 10 minutes.

3. Preheat the oven to 176°F (80°C).

4. Let the refrigerated juice preparation sit on the counter for 30 minutes or until it warms up to a 57.2°F (14°C).

5. Pour the preparation into the bowl of a mixer. Using the mixer's whisk attachment, start whipping the mixture. As the foam starts forming, progressively start adding the mix of juice and cold soluble gelatin. Continue whipping for 10 minutes.

6. Pour the preparation onto a parchment-paper-lined baking sheet. Spread a thin layer of the preparation using a spatula. Let dry in the oven for at least 1 hour.

SERVING SUGGESTION

Once dried, cover the peach sheet with a second layer of parchment paper. Use a rolling pin to flatten it out, then cut it into rectangular pieces.

METHYLCELLULOSE MERINGUE

Add the **METHYLCELLULOSE** to one half of the preparation and the **COLD SOLUBLE GELATIN** to the other half.

Refrigerate the **METHYLCELLULOSE** mixture then, let it come back to room temperature

Let the **COLD SOLUBLE GELATIN** mixture sit for 10 minutes

Whip the **METHYLCELLULOSE** mixture

Gradually add the **COLD SOLUBLE GELATIN** mixture to the **METHYLCELLULOSE** one while whipping

OTHER TRANSFORMATIONS
Recipes

COFFEE SMOOTHNESS

DIFFICULTY	
PREP TIME	5 MIN
REST TIME	30 MIN

ADDITIVE	Sl

TOOLS	

TIPS & TRICKS	P. 64

INGREDIENTS

Espresso coffee	1¼ cup (300 ml)
Sugar	2 tbsp (30 ml)
Tia Maria	½ cup (120 ml)

ADDITIVE

SOY LECITHIN	2 g (1 sachet)

DIRECTIONS

1. Combine all the ingredients and the **SOY LECITHIN** in a bowl and mix.
2. Pour the mixture through a sieve into the culinary whipper.
3. Close the culinary whipper, load one N2O gas cartridge and shake for 4 seconds.
4. Refrigerate for 30 minutes before serving.

SERVING SUGGESTION

Serve the coffee smoothness into clear glasses so that the separation between the liquid coffee and the espuma is visible.

SIPHON WHIPPING

Filter the preparation through a sieve before pouring it into the culinary whipper

Close the whipper, load 1 gas cartridge, shake and refrigerate

Press on the lever to serve

COLA WHIP

INGREDIENTS

Cola	¾ cup (180 ml)
35% cooking cream	¾ cup (180 ml)

DIRECTIONS

1. Combine all the ingredients in a bowl and mix.
2. Pour the mixture into the culinary whipper.
3. Close the culinary whipper, load one N2O gas cartridge and shake for 4 seconds.
4. Refrigerate for 30 minutes before serving.

SERVING SUGGESTION

Pour the cola whip into clear glasses and decorate with a soda can tab to mimic a soda can.

DIFFICULTY
PREP TIME 5 MIN
REST TIME 30 MIN

ADDITIVE

TOOLS

TIPS & TRICKS P. 64

SIPHON WHIPPING

Filter the preparation through a sieve before pouring it into the culinary whipper

Close the whipper, load 1 gas cartridge, shake and refrigerate

Press on the lever to serve

ESPUMA OF THE SEAS

DIFFICULTY	
PREP TIME	10 MIN
REST TIME	30 MIN

ADDITIVE

TOOLS

TIPS & TRICKS P. 64

INGREDIENTS

35% cooking cream	2 cups (470 ml)
Cod, diced	7 oz (200 g)
Saffron	1 pinch
Green onion, chopped	1
Garlic, chopped	1 clove
Salt	to taste
Pepper	to taste
Paprika	to taste

DIRECTIONS

1. In a pan, bring all ingredients to a boil except for the paprika. Cook on low heat for 15 minutes.
2. Pour the mixture through a sieve into the culinary whipper.
3. Close the culinary whipper, load one N2O gas cartridge and shake for 4 seconds.
4. Refrigerate for 30 minutes before serving.

SERVING SUGGESTION

Serve the espuma in verrines and sprinkle with paprika.

SIPHON WHIPPING

Filter the preparation through a sieve before pouring it into the culinary whipper

Close the whipper, load 1 gas cartridge, shake and refrigerate

Press on the lever to serve

GUINNESS ESPUMA

INGREDIENTS

Guinness beer	1¼ cups (300 ml)
Sweetened condensed milk	4.25 oz (120 g)
Chocolate ice cream	1 tub

DIRECTIONS

1. Pour the condensed milk into a bowl, then steadily add the beer while stirring constantly.
2. Pour the mixture through a sieve into the culinary whipper.
3. Close the culinary whipper, load one N2O gas cartridge and shake for 4 seconds.
4. Refrigerate for 30 minutes before serving.

SERVING SUGGESTION

Fill small, clear glasses with chocolate ice cream and top the verrines off with the Guiness espuma.

DIFFICULTY	
PREP TIME	5 MIN
REST TIME	30 MIN

ADDITIVE

TOOLS

TIPS & TRICKS   P. 64

SIPHON WHIPPING

Filter the preparation through a sieve before pouring it into the culinary whipper

Close the whipper, load 1 gas cartridge, shake and refrigerate

Press on the lever to serve

CUTTING EDGE PORTO-CHEDDAR

INGREDIENTS

CHEDDAR ESPUMA

35% cooking cream	1 cup (235 ml)
Cheddar cheese, grated	3.5 oz (100 g)

GELIFIED PORT WINE

Port wine	1 cup (235 ml)
Sugar	0.5 oz (15 g)

ADDITIVE

COLD SOLUBLE GELATIN	6 g (1 ½ sachet)

DIFFICULTY		
PREP TIME	15 MIN	
REST TIME	30 MIN	
ADDITIVE	G	
TOOLS		
TIPS & TRICKS	P. 64	

DIRECTIONS

CHEDDAR ESPUMA

1. In a saucepan, melt the cheddar. Bring to a boil and mix the cream in.
2. Pour the mixture through a sieve into the culinary whipper.
3. Close the culinary whipper, load one N2O gas cartridge and shake for 4 seconds.
4. Refrigerate for 30 minutes before serving.

GELIFIED PORT WINE

1. Using a spoon, dissolve the **COLD SOLUBLE GELATIN** into the port. Let sit for 5 minutes.
2. Fill small, clear glasses a third full with the mixture and place in the freezer for 1 hour or until the mixture is completely congealed.

SERVING SUGGESTION

Decorate the port verrines with a generous layer of the cheddar espuma.

SIPHON WHIPPING

Filter the preparation through a sieve before pouring it into the culinary whipper

Close the whipper, load 1 gas cartridge, shake and refrigerate

Press on the lever to serve

INGREDIENTS

Croutons	4

FOIE GRAS ESPUMA

35% cooking cream	1 cup (235 ml)
Foie gras, diced	7 oz (200 g)
Salt	to taste
Pepper	to taste

FIG JELLY

Dried figs, chopped	2
Water	1 cup (235 ml)
Sugar	1 tbsp (15 ml)

ADDITIVE

AGAR-AGAR	2 g (1 sachet)

DIFFICULTY	👨‍🍳👨‍🍳
PREP TIME	20 MIN
REST TIME	30 MIN

ADDITIVE	Aa

TOOLS	

TIPS & TRICKS	*(1)* P. 64
	(2) P. 22

DIRECTIONS

FOIE GRAS ESPUMA [1]

1. Place the cream in a pan and bring to a boil.
2. Turn off the heat and mix in the foie gras, salt and pepper.
3. Pour the mixture through a sieve into the culinary whipper.
4. Close the culinary whipper, load one N2O gas cartridge and shake for 4 seconds.
5. Refrigerate for 30 minutes before serving.

FIG JELLY [2]

1. In a saucepan, bring the water to a boil. Incorporate all the other ingredients, plus the **AGAR-AGAR**, and cook for 5 minutes while stirring.
2. Spread the mixture onto a small baking sheet and let cool, then unmold and cut into desired shapes.

SERVING SUGGESTION

Serve croutons garnished with the fig jelly and the foie gras espuma.

SIPHON WHIPPING [1]

Filter the preparation through a sieve before pouring it into the culinary whipper

Close the whipper, load 1 gas cartridge, shake and refrigerate

Press on the lever to serve

MOJITO SMOOTHNESS

INGREDIENTS

Water	¼ cup (60 ml)
Sugar	2.5 oz (70 g)
Egg whites	5
Lemon juice	½ cup (120 ml)
White rum	⅓ cup (80 ml)
Pineapple, diced	½ cup (120 ml)
Fresh mint, chopped	to taste

DIFFICULTY

PREP TIME   15 MIN

REST TIME   30 MIN

ADDITIVE

TOOLS

TIPS & TRICKS   P. 64

DIRECTIONS

1. Bring the water and sugar to a boil. Remove from the stove and refrigerate for 30 minutes.

2. In a bowl, beat the egg whites with the lemon juice and rum.

3. Pour the mixture through a sieve into the culinary whipper.

4. Close the culinary whipper, load one N2O gas cartridge and shake for 4 seconds.

5. Refrigerate for 30 minutes before serving.

SERVING SUGGESTION

Distribute the pineapple dices on a plate, top with the mojito espuma and decorate with fresh mint.

SIPHON WHIPPING

Filter the preparation through a sieve before pouring it into the culinary whipper

Close the whipper, load 1 gas cartridge, shake and refrigerate

Press on the lever to serve

MOLECULAR PARFAIT AND COCO ESPUMA

INGREDIENTS

Passion fruit sherbet	1 tub

COCONUT ESPUMA

Coconut milk	1 cup (235 ml)
Sugar	2 tbsp (30 ml)
Vanilla extract	4 drops

FROZEN RASPBERRIES

Raspberries	3.5 oz (100 g)

ADDITIVES

COLD SOLUBLE GELATIN	4 g (1 sachet)
LIQUID NITROGEN	optional

DIFFICULTY		
PREP TIME	15 MIN	
REST TIME	45 MIN	
ADDITIVE		G Ln
TOOLS		
TIPS & TRICKS	P. 64	

DIRECTIONS

COCONUT ESPUMA

1. Place the coconut milk and sugar in a pan and bring them to a boil. Take the pan off the fire and mix in the vanilla extract and **COLD SOLUBLE GELATIN**.
2. Pour the mixture through a sieve into the culinary whipper.
3. Close the culinary whipper, load one N2O gas cartridge and shake for 4 seconds.
4. Refrigerate for 45 minutes before serving.

FROZEN RASPBERRIES

1. Use **LIQUID NITROGEN** to freeze the raspberries or, alternatively, leave them in the freezer for 24 hours prior to serving.
2. Crush the frozen raspberries.

SERVING SUGGESTION

In a tall, clear glass, layer the frozen raspberries and sherbet and top it off with the coconut espuma.

SIPHON WHIPPING

Filter the preparation through a sieve before pouring it into the culinary whipper

Close the whipper, load 1 gas cartridge, shake and refrigerate

Press on the lever to serve

INGREDIENTS

DRESSING

Egg yolk	1
Dijon mustard	1 tbsp (15 ml)
Red wine vinegar	2 tbsp (30 ml)
Tabasco	5 drops
Worcestershire sauce	10 drops
Anchovy filets, chopped	4
Garlic, chopped	2 cloves
Capers, chopped	1 tbsp (15 ml)
Salt	to taste
Pepper	to taste
Vegetable oil	1 cup (235 ml)

TOPPINGS

Whole romaine lettuce	1
Water	¼ cup (160 ml)
Crisp bacon, chopped	4 slices
Parmesan, grated	¼ cup (160 ml)
Croutons, chopped	¼ cup (160 ml)

ADDITIVE

XANTHAN GUM	1 g (1 sachet)

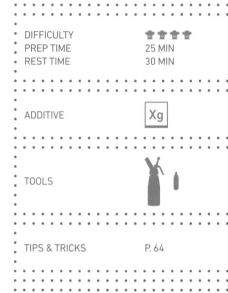

DIFFICULTY	♟ ♟ ♟ ♟
PREP TIME	25 MIN
REST TIME	30 MIN

ADDITIVE — Xg

TOOLS

TIPS & TRICKS — P. 64

DIRECTIONS

1. Pour all ingredients for the dressing into a blender. Mix for 1 minute or until the mixture is smooth.

2. Pour the mixture into a bowl and mix it using a hand blender, while drizzling with olive oil to make the dressing. Reserve.

3. In another bowl, mix the chopped romaine lettuce and water using a hand blender for 1 minute. Add the dressing and mix one minute more. Add more water, if needed.

4. Mix in the **XANTHAN GUM** using a hand blender.

5. Pour the mixture through a sieve and reserve no more than 2 cups (470 ml). Pour the filtered mixture into the culinary whipper.

6. Close the culinary whipper, load one N2O gas cartridge and shake for 4 seconds.

7. Refrigerate for 30 minutes. before serving.

SERVING SUGGESTION

For a deconstructed salad, arrange on a plate one slice of bacon, a few chopped croutons and the Ceasar espuma.

SIPHON WHIPPING

Filter the preparation through a sieve before pouring it into the culinary whipper

Close the whipper, load 1 gas cartridge, shake and refrigerate

Press on the lever to serve

DECONSTRUCTED PEACH

INGREDIENTS

Water	2½ cups (590 ml)
Sugar	2.85 oz (80 g)
Peaches	12 oz (375 g)

ADDITIVES

COLD SOLUBLE GELATIN	6 g + 8 g (3½ sachets)

DIRECTIONS

PEACH GELATIN

1. Dice the peaches.
2. Bring the water, sugar and peaches to a boil. Cook on low heat for 1 hour. Remove from stove and refrigerate for 30 minutes.
3. Pour off 1 cup (235 ml) of the cooking syrup and strain it through a sieve. Reserve the rest of the syrup and the cooked peaches.
4. Using a spoon, incorporate 6 g (1½ sachets) of the **COLD SOLUBLE GELATIN** into the filtered syrup and pour into a square container. Mix in 2.1oz (60 g) of the cooked peaches and refrigerate for 2 hours or until the preparation is completely congealed.
5. Unmold the congealed preparation and cut it into rectangular pieces.

PEACH ESPUMA

1. Place 1 cup (235 ml) of the cooking syrup in a blender and process until a coulis is obtained.
2. Strain the coulis through a sieve, then use a hand blender to mix in 8 g (2 sachets) of the **COLD SQLUBLE GELATIN**. Let sit for 5 minutes.
3. Pour the mixture through a sieve into the culinary whipper
4. Close the culinary whipper, load one N2O gas cartridge and shake for 4 seconds.
5. Refrigerate for 30 minutes before serving.

SERVING SUGGESTION

Serve the peach espuma as a verrine along with the peach gelatin.

DIFFICULTY	
PREP TIME	30 MIN
REST TIME	2 HOURS

ADDITIVE	G

TOOLS	

TIPS & TRICKS	P. 64

SIPHON WHIPPING

Filter the preparation through a sieve before pouring it into the culinary whipper

Close the whipper, load 1 gas cartridge, shake and refrigerate

Press on the lever to serve

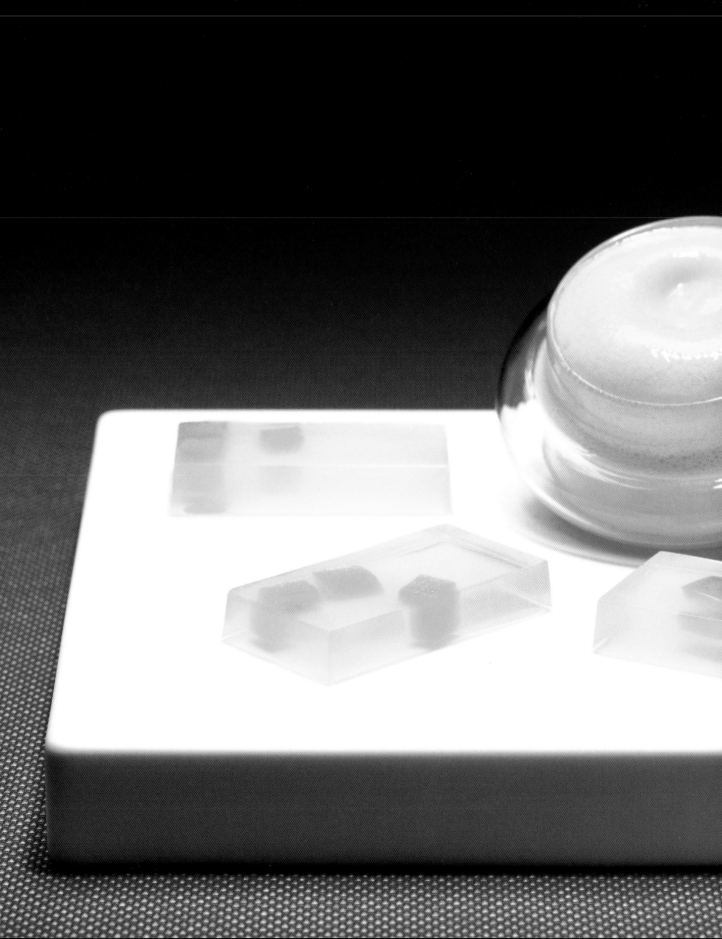

REINVENTED CHOCO-HAZELNUT

INGREDIENTS

NUTELLA CAKE

Nutella	7 oz (200 g)
Egg whites	4
Egg yolks	5
Sugar	3 oz (80 g)
Flour	0.75 oz (20 g)

NUTELLA ESPUMA

35% cooking cream	1 cup (235 ml)
Nutella	7 oz (200 g)

NUTELLA POWDER

Nutella	0.5 oz (15 g)

ADDITIVE

TAPIOCA MALTODEXTRIN	100 g (3.5 oz)

DIFFICULTY	
PREP TIME	40 MIN
REST TIME	1 HOUR
ADDITIVE	M
TOOLS	
TIPS & TRICKS	P. 64

DIRECTIONS

NUTELLA CAKE

1. Pour all ingredients into a blender and mix until smooth.

2. Pour the mixture through a sieve into the culinary whipper.

3. Close the culinary whipper, load one N2O gas cartridge and shake for 4 seconds. Refrigerate for 30 minutes.

4. After 30 minutes, remove the culinary whipper from the fridge and fill a plastic cup three-fourths full with the refrigerated cake mixture.

5. Cook in a microwave oven at maximum power for 40 seconds. Unmold the cake as soon as it is removed from the microwave oven.

NUTELLA ESPUMA

1. In a double boiler, heat the cream and Nutella while stirring until completely blended.

2. Pour the mixture through a sieve into the culinary whipper.

3. Close the culinary whipper, load one N2O gas cartridge and shake for 4 seconds.

4. Refrigerate for 30 minutes before serving.

NUTELLA POWDER

1. Using a fork, gradually mix the **TAPIOCA MALTODEXTRIN** with 0.5 oz (15 g) of Nutella until a powder is obtained.

SERVING SUGGESTION

Dust a plate with a thin later of Nutella powder and place the Nutella cake and some of the Nutella espuma on it.

SIPHON WHIPPING

Filter the preparation
through a sieve before
pouring it into the
culinary whipper

Close the whipper, load
1 gas cartridge, shake
and refrigerate

Press on the lever
to serve

MOLECULE-R FIRST RECIPE CONTEST

FANS' CHOICE:

BLUEBERRY VERRINES WITH STRAWBERRY CAVIAR

By   Alan Topalovic
From   Woodridge, IL

ABOUT THE CHEF

Alan is 17 years old and he's always liked how molecular gastronomy looked and wanted to try it. He attends two high schools, one for general studies and the other for culinary / pastry arts, hoping to become a pastry chef soon.

VIEW THE DETAILED RECIPE

JURY'S CHOICE:

BACARDI AND COKE COCKTAIL

By   Daniel Bartlett
From   Colorado Springs, CO

ABOUT THE CHEF

Chef Daniel Bartlett specialty is unique food art with an elite style of modern cooking. He is the next Willy Wonka, Dr. Seuss, and the Mad Hatter combined, playing with food in ways that will trick the senses from light airy foams, to textures, colors and flavors that will keep you guessing and on the edge of your seat. Chef Dan is an innovative chef exploding in the culinary world.

VIEW THE DETAILED RECIPE

JOIN US ON FACEBOOK
BE THE FIRST TO GET UPDATES
ON PROMO AND NEW PRODUCTS

SIPHON R-EVOLUTION

ADD A CREAMY TOUCH
TO YOUR DESSERTS,
APPETIZERS AND
SIDE DISHES !

*EACH KIT CONTAINS A CULINARY
WHIPPER AND ITS ACCESSORIES.*

*3 NATURAL FOOD ADDITIVES IN PRE-MEASURED SACHETS
AGAR-AGAR, COLD SOLUBLE GELATIN AND XANTHAN GUM.*

A RECIPE BOOKLET.

6 N2O GAS CARTRIDGES.

Copyright © 2014, 2013 by MOLECULE-R Flavors Inc.
ISBN : 978-0-9921110-1-4

SECOND EDITION - 2014

MOLECULE-R Flavors Inc.
2255A, Dandurand St.
Montreal (Qc) Canada
H2G 1Z3

MOLECULE-R.COM